OAKWOOD REMINISCENCES

Testing Times at Derby

A 'Privileged' View of Steam

by
Alan Rimmer

THE OAKWOOD PRESS

British Library Cataloguing in Publication Data
A Record for this book is available from the British Library
ISBN 0 85361 628 0

Typeset by Oakwood Graphics.
Repro by Ford Graphics, Ringwood, Hants.
Printed by Cambrian Printers Ltd, Aberystwyth, Ceredigion.

'B1' class No. 61353 at Rugby Test Plant having completed a day of testing, moving out of the test hall to go to the preparation shed. *Author*

Title page: BR Standard 'Britannia' class 4-6-2 No. 70043 fitted with two Westinghouse pumps, with a train of 16 ton 'Minfit' wagons at Ilkeston Junction while carrying out static and slow speed tests in 1955. *P. Webb*

Published by The Oakwood Press (Usk), P.O. Box 13, Usk, Mon., NP15 1YS.
E-mail: oakwood-press@dial.pipex.com
Website: www.oakwood-press.dial.pipex.com

Contents

	Foreword	3
Chapter One	**An Engineering Apprentice**	5
Chapter Two	**Learning the Trade**	11
Chapter Three	**I Join the Drawing Office Staff**	21
Chapter Four	**Some Memories of Locomotive Testing**	33
Chapter Five	**The Mobile Testing Plant**	43
Chapter Six	**Testing the First 'Britannia'**	55
Chapter Seven	**Locomotive Testing on the Settle & Carlisle**	65
Chapter Eight	**Some Unofficial 'Driving Turns'**	81
Chapter Nine	**The Farnborough Indicator**	91
Chapter Ten	**Axleboxes, Boilers & Brakes**	102
Chapter Eleven	**Steam Finale**	115

Foreword

The contents of this book first appeared as a series of articles in a model engineering magazine, *Locomotives Large and Small*, in the 1980s. There has been a certain amount of revision, but readers will have to bear in mind the original concept and accept that references to 'small locomotives' refer to miniature steam-driven machines running on 3½ in. and 5 in. gauge tracks, whilst a reference to a large locomotive will be one built to a scale of 12 inches to the foot!

In LMS days, Johnson '1P' class 0-4-4T No. 1252 is seen after repairs with scrubbed and revarnished transfers and 'patch painted' in accordance with the economies of the mid-1940s.
Author

LMS No. 4585, a '4F' 'Big Goods' with scrubbed number and letter transfers. the tender is fitted with a fuel oil tank during the short-lived oil burning period due to coal shortages in the 1940s.
Author

Chapter One

An Engineering Apprentice

It was in September 1943 that I gave up the status of schoolboy and became a 'Priv'. What on earth, you may ask, is a Priv? Enlightenment - it was a form of life otherwise known as Engineering Apprentice and I joined the ranks of these in the London Midland & Scottish Railway (LMS) locomotive works at Derby. The term 'Priv' was applied to us by most of the work force, and dated back to the time when there was a Privileged Apprentice position. At the time of my apprenticeship there were us 'Privs', about 50 of us all told, and there was a much larger number of Trade Apprentices. The main difference was in the content of the course, the 'Priv' was given a very general engineering training with three months or thereabouts on each section in machine and fitting shops, boiler and boiler mounting, bogie, iron foundry, millwrights, welding, wheel and erecting shops while the Trade lads had their training planned with a view to becoming qualified in their choice of trade, e.g. fitter, turner, electrician, millwright or whatever. The Engineering apprenticeship resulted in the 'Priv' becoming a locomotive erector on his 21st birthday.

Having presented myself at the appointed time - on the first morning, you reported to the Offices, so did not have to be there until nine o'clock - I found there were three other starters. We were taken down to the machine shop main office and then re-deployed, two of us ending up in 'Grease Corner'. Most apprentices cut their teeth down here, tapping nuts and threading bolts of various sizes. Most of these machines used copious quantities of a thick brown cutting oil which seemed to get everywhere, hence the name. Sometimes you could just about wring oil out of overalls if you wore them for a whole week.

I was fortunate and was set on to a large centre lathe, probably about 9 or 10 inches and capable of taking about four feet between centres. Never having had any experience of lathe work, or any form of workshop work, I was immediately set on screw cutting internal threads in large nuts, for spring hanger bolts. Having faced one side and cut the thread on a batch, they were then mounted on a mandrel and the taper seating on the other end was machined with the compound slide. The tool-setter who acted as chargeman was very patient with me, and I am pleased to say I soon got the hang of it. I remember vaguely scrapping a batch of these big nuts, which were about 2 in. diameter thread because I evolved a 'short-cut' to determine the correct length, but I got something fundamentally wrong and took a lot too much off!

Then I got on to external threads on boiler stays. These had a length of thread at each end to screw into the firebox crown and the outer wrapper, with a long plain piece in between which was slightly smaller in diameter than the core diameter of the thread. The thread on the two portions had to match as if it was continuous, and it was also slightly tapered so that as the stays were screwed home, they formed a steam-tight seal. The threads were cut with a single point tool, each part being done separately to a gauge, one for each bit and then finished with a hand held chasing tool to another pair of gauges. I learnt a lot of

An LMS Fowler '2P' class 4-4-0 No. 682 stripped for repairs in No. 1 Bay, of the Derby erecting shop. The 'M' above the number indicated that this was a London Midland Region engine in the newly-formed British Railways. *Author*

Fully painted Midland 'Jinty' No. 47225 poses in Derby Loco yard complete with its 'galloping lion' British Railways emblem in the 1950s. *Author*

basic centre lathe work in my three months with that machine, which incidentally was over 30 years old, driven by flat belt and three step pulleys from overhead line shafting. There was a fast and loose pulley drive to the overhead pulley which responded to a tug on one side or the other of a loop of chain which hung just over your head. Changes of speed were effected by flicking the belt down a step at the lathe, then more flicks with the hand to get it to the chosen step up top, and a final flick to the corresponding diameter on the headstock. Again, the knack was soon acquired, but I should imagine that it would make a factory inspector shudder today with legislation like the Health and Safety at Work Act in force, just to think about it, never mind see it in action!

So I was on my way and every three months moved to another section of the machine and fitting shop, all the time acquiring new and different skills. I spent most of my time on brass turning, drilling holes at first on a clapped out old machine which disappeared one weekend, being replaced by a brand new one. This meant that my speed of work shot up, and my bonus rate went so high that the chargehand used to refuse to give me another job straight away, and then hauled me over the coals either for standing about talking to other apprentices, or for disappearing for too long. However, he realised why it was and in the end the bonus I earned was spread over other men on the section, much to their delight. Brass fitting I remember again by bonus earnings. Another 'Priv' and myself teamed up and by so doing found that we could earn much higher rates in this way. Our favourite was sand-traps, the device which controlled the flow of sand out of a sand box, where we found that we could do a batch of, I think it was 20, for which we were allowed about 12 hours, in about two! Here again, the chargehand was sometimes a bit embarrassed by it all, and occasionally invited us to disappear for a bit, taking the risk that we would be seen by a foreman somewhere where we should not have been, and that we would not say that Fred had told us to make ourselves scarce!

And so it went on, through axleboxes, motion, jigs and fixtures and the tool room. While in the last named, I made the inevitable cigarette lighter (to the standard design from a block of aluminium) and also made a single acting steam engine with pieces of gauge plate screwed together to form its frame and a chunk of brass for the cylinder block. I am pleased to say that it did, and still does, run well and I suppose it represents my first step in model engineering. It was based on a design in *Model Engineer* of around that time and I sometimes think I ought to go through my back numbers and find the original, but never seem to find the time.

The spell on jigs and fixtures was, to my mind, one of the most fascinating. It was only a small group, about 10 in number and everyone a real craftsman. I was put to work with Fred Churchman, who was an ex-Guardsman as you could see by his stance and the shine of his boots. He was a hard worker and did not approve of other 'Privs' calling for a chat unless it was only for a couple of minutes, but I learnt a lot from Fred.

As the name implies, we were involved in the making of jigs, which enabled a repetitive line of items to be produced to be identical, whereas fixtures were made to help with holding a workpiece for machining to marked-out detail.

Starting work on the railway led to a very rapid increase in interest which centred locally on the Cromford & High Peak line (which culminated in my writing *The Cromford & High Peak Railway*, Oakwood Press (LP10), which was first published in 1956 and is still in print today). This line had two notable features, one being the 1 in 14 Hopton Incline, the other, the 'Chopper' tank, the last of its class by many years, it worked the isolated stretch between Sheep Pasture and Middleton inclines. When I first knew it, the engine was numbered 6428. This study shows it in late 1949 carrying its BR number, and standing at Sheep Pasture Top.
Harry Pitt

Fred would give me a drawing from the jig and tool office and leave me to study it for a time. Then we would talk about how I would tackle the job and guidance would be given as to how my ideas should be modified, an indication given as to where to get the material I needed, and then I was on my own! Fred would come over now and then to see how I was getting on, and we always had a few minutes at the start of each day, but that apart, I was left to get on at my own pace. As I said, I learnt a tremendous amount in that period.

Having had a total of 18 months in the machine and fitting shop, I then moved on into the rest of the works. There was not time to go into every shop in a five year apprenticeship, but there was a fair variety, certainly in my case. I can't be certain of the chronological order but I can at least identify where I went.

One of the first was the millwrights shop, and here I was put as mate to a fitter called Cyril. We concentrated our attention on the repair of hydraulic capstans, such as were used up and down the railway system in goods yards for hauling wagons, being powered by a hydraulic pump driven by an electric motor, and usually having a hydraulic accumulator in the system as well.

The latter was a tall vertical cylinder, having a piston almost as long as the cylinder, with a circular ring at the top which carried a series of annular cast iron weights which surrounded the cylinder, but did not touch it. This device was 'proper hydraulic', using water as the working fluid. In use in the goods yards, with strategically placed 'free capstan' pulleys the rope could be arranged to move the wagons away from the power capstan as well as towards it. The same system would also be used to operate hydraulic lifts in goods sheds and stations, and on occasion Cyril and I went to carry out running repairs. In all, I spent two months here, and then had a further month with the small group of millwrights permanently employed in the boiler and wheel shops. This was different work again, being concerned purely with maintenance of machines. As the 'lad' I was put to dressing and re-fitting grinding wheels on which the wheel-lathe operators kept their tools sharpened. Woe betide me if I forgot to go my 'round' one morning - we were soon told of any hollow wheels.

While in the millwrights we were expected to work every weekend, and several interesting jobs cropped up in this way. One Saturday and Sunday, we were involved in dismantling two large vertical boilers in the carriage and wagon works, the boilers being outside the shop and our staging was a series of planks laid across four stays between the boilers and the shop wall. I suppose we were about 25 ft above the ground, and my most vivid memory is of when I stood to one side to let my mate get at something and I stepped on a short plank which was overhanging the stays! Fortunately, Cyril saw what was happening, stamped on the plank which was rearing up and grabbed me at the same time! These days of course, with the Health and Safety at Work Act, the planks would no doubt be clamped to the stays, and a safety rail around the platform would also be a statutory requirement! Anyway, I sat with my back to the wall for a few minutes while the jelly in my legs set.

After millwrighting, I moved into the central materials inspection bureau, which was a haven of peace compared to the noise of the places I had been before. This was a quite different world, where I was instructed in the techniques of crushing cubes of concrete to determine the strength of a cast, in some cases using a sequence of blocks at pre-determined periods to assess how strength was increasing with time. We also prepared metal specimens for tensile testing and carried out the tests themselves. Apart from the inspectors, there were just three of us, Lol the turner, a fitter whose name I can't recall, and myself.

A bonus was that our workshop was just at the back of Derby station and trains went by only feet from the window. In the course of the previous months, I had begun to take more interest in trains and locomotives, which had not taken much of my attention during school days. But now I was beginning to develop a deeper interest as I began to identify different classes of locomotive, to find out the secrets of 'shed plates' and allocations to depots, and generally to delve into the mechanics of the machine to find out what made it work. This absorption of Steam into the Blood is an insidious process, as I hope to show in the following chapters.

Ex-Mersey Railway 0-6-4T working as NCB No. 42 at Shipley Colliery. It was No. 5 *Cecil Raikes* on the Mersey Railway, and was built by Beyer, Peacock at Gorton in 1886. It retained its prominent condensing pipes as the colliery manager said; it did not look right without them. *Author*

Chapter Two

Learning the Trade

I don't know if it was planned that way, but I moved from the quiet calm of the central materials inspection bureau, where the loudest noises were the crack of a tensile specimen snapping or the monotonous graunch-graunch-graunch of the file testing machine, into the cacophony of the boiler shop. On first stepping into this place, the noise seemed to bear down on you in a physical manner, and when you stepped outside, the relief was incredible, although it took several minutes, or so it seemed, for the 'ringing' in your ears to subside. After a few days, I became used to it, and could walk through the door without reeling backwards!

The noise came from the rivetters mainly; during my spell in the boiler shop, the construction of new tender tanks was in full swing and there were also some new side tanks and bunkers being made as well. Derby did not build new boilers, that work being carried out at Crewe, but heavy repairs were undertaken which involved the removal of tubes and fireboxes, so that the boiler was rebuilt from a shell onwards. Again, the pneumatic chisels used to remove scale from the plates of a stripped out boiler added to the noise, which was at an incredible level, and yet little or no effort was made to cut it down, nor was there any general use made of ear plugs or the like. Some of the men plugged their ears with cotton wool, but I don't think that was particularly effective. In the more enlightened times in which we now live, I cannot imagine that management would be allowed to subject its workforce to such a noisy environment, even if the workforce were docile enough not to complain.

I spent my time in the boiler shop with the finished work inspectors, which involved checking for squareness, tightness of rivets (done with a small hammer, the loose rivet giving a different sound) and observing the hydraulic tests of tanks, to see that these were watertight at all the joints. There were also a lot of small jobs, 'one-offs' and the like, and I was soon left to get on with the inspection of these on my own. It seemed odd to me that here was I about two years out of school, examining work carried out by men with 10 or 15 times that length of experience. However, there were no 'come-backs' and the two inspectors kept a fatherly eye on what I was doing and soon pointed out if they thought my examination technique could be improved.

I then made the natural progression from the boiler shop next door into boiler mounting. Here it was that the boiler was re-fitted with its various internal tubes and pipes, items like regulator stands, safety valves and all the various blobs and gadgets on the backhead. Much of the work involved the preparation of jointing faces on the mounting pads on the backhead. First job was to remove any studs or shell-out the remains where a stud was broken off. The technique was to drill into the broken stub so that the drill just touched the bottom of the thread, the drill being about two-thirds the diameter of the thread core. Then by judicious use of a round nose chisel, it was possible to drive the metal towards the hole and break the threads, this usually being sufficient to enable the stub to be unscrewed with little or no thread damage.

The author on the footplate of Romney, Hythe & Dymchurch Railway 4-6-2 No. 10 *Doctor Syn* during a weekend visit in 1946.
Author

An unusual view of 'Jubilee' class 4-6-0 No. 5611 *Hong Kong* taking water at Appleby. This was a footplate trip undertaken when I was an apprentice one Saturday, between Leeds and Carlisle.
Author

Having removed all the studs, the pad was then carefully filed as flat as possible - no easy job, as the surface was near vertical, and one was often standing on a temporary platform of planks. Just lifting the iron faceplate up and down to keep checking progress was as good as taking the Charles Atlas course! Some of the mounting pads were quite large, such as for injector steam valves which took steam from the boiler, and also admitted injector feed while most of the others just had a single opening. Once all the faces had been completed, then new studs were fitted. Another face which required similar attention was for the main steam pipe at the smokebox end, which was the largest of the lot, but did have a big hole through it! It also involved the use of the biggest face plate, although the actual joint area was reasonable, being a relatively narrow ring.

I spent some time working on superheater headers, renewing studs and re-cutting the element seats. Most of these were face-to-face, although there were still some headers which had a copper ring fitted into a groove in the header and a similar groove on the element tube end. Having spent some time machining these rings in the machine shop, I now saw where they went!

It was while working on the headers that I received the worst injury of all that I suffered as an apprentice. When a stud refused to unscrew, even with a tube on the end of the spanner on the extractor, it either twisted off flush, or it was notched with a chisel and then clouted with a sledge hammer. My mate was performing this latter operation, having instructed me to stand behind him where, presumably, he reckoned I would be safe. I wasn't and was struck forcibly by a flying stud just at the side of the right eye. Off to the ambulance room, then a trip to the local Infirmary for five stitches and a lump the size of an egg on the side of my face for a few days. As it happened, the following evening was the Annual Engineering Apprentices Dance at which I was MC. I looked a bit of a card in dinner jacket and a mass of sticking plaster.

Another 'escapade' involved one of my fellow 'Privs', one Basil Watson. He was working on the dome of this particular boiler and dropped his chisel which landed on top of the tube nest. Now when this happened, you usually went to fetch a pair of long handled tongs kept for the purpose and retrieved the dropped tool. But not Baz! He reckoned he could reach it without climbing down off the boiler and walking the length of the shop for the tongs. He puts his arms above his head, high-diver fashion, and into the dome which was quite a tall one, wriggles his shoulders down and finds at full stretch his finger tips just touch the chisel, but he can't get his fingers round it. So one more wriggle and he has hold of it, but at the cost of losing his balance. It is soon obvious to the men round about, and the word spreads like wildfire, work stops and a crowd soon gathers. One or two hammer on the boiler to add to his predicament, but no-one goes to give him the heave he needs to regain his balance and get himself out. Instead, the overhead crane is brought down to where his legs are now waving in the air, a large rope sling is secured round his ankles and he is extracted, very red in the face. To complete his discomforture, he is then carried on the crane the length of the shop before being lowered to the ground. I think he always used the tongs after that - I certainly did!

My next move was into the iron foundry. The training scheme here seemed to me to be a little bit sketchy and I got the impression that the foreman would

The Locomotive Interchange Trials I. LNER 'B1' class 4-6-0 No. 61251 *Oliver Bury* leaves Derby for Manchester Central in June 1948. This was not a test run, but was for driver and fireman familiarisation in the week prior to tests proper. *Author*

The Locomotive Interchange Trials II. Southern Railway 'West Country' class 4-6-2 No. 34005 *Barnstaple* leaves Derby for Manchester Central on 22nd June, 1948, the first of four days of test running with No. 1 Dynamometer Car. *Author*

have liked it far better if 'Privs' had never been invented, or at least had never set foot in his domain. We generally found that it was better if we kept what is now called a 'low profile'.

It was wintertime when I was iron-founding, and I spent the first few weeks in the core shop, picking up the fundamentals of core-making, starting with the simple cylindrical forms, and progressing to some of the quite complicated shapes such as were used to form the steam ways in cylinder castings. These cores were themselves formed around a spider-like casting, usually cast 'open' on the foundry floor, and also had to be provided with vents, which were formed by running lengths of wax-coated string through the core as it was built up, so that during the baking, the wax would melt and be burnt out. Core sand was bound with oil rather than water, and after baking, was often finished using old files, which were very rapidly 'finished off' by the abrasive core. Simple cylindrical cores were often made in long lengths and sawn into shorter pieces with a hacksaw. Again, blades lasted no time at all.

The cores were baked in ovens which were large rooms about seven feet high, maybe 10 feet wide and 12 feet long, with heavy steel doors at each end. The source of heat was a sort of huge brazier down the length of one wall which must have held about a ton of coke. This was kept burning during the day while the cores were being made and stacked on their trays in the oven, with the doors open. In the late afternoon the brazier was filled with barrow loads of coke, and then the doors were shut. On opening up the following morning the fire would be well burnt through, and the cores all baked hard. In the time I was there, we spent most of the first hour or so in the oven itself, particularly on frosty mornings. I wonder the fumes did not poison us!

After core-making, I went to work with one of the moulders, helping him to earn his bonus. He was an elderly fellow, a bit taciturn, but once we got to know each other, we got on well. He showed me how to set about ramming up the 'cope' and the 'drag', the difference between parting sand and backing sand, how parting powder helped in separating the halves of the box, and how the application of graphite powder, subsequently smoothed down, would improve the casting surface. I also learnt the importance of venting the box, without jabbing the spike into the pattern, how to 'rap' the pattern before removal, and also how to judge the moisture content so that the box would not 'blow'. While I was in the foundry, we had a cylinder mould which 'blew' and most spectacular it was too. The cause was sand which was too moist, which produced more steam than the vents could cope with, so that several hundredweight of red hot iron formed a fountain out of the riser. Fortunately, there was no injury, but the moulder was subjected to some scathing remarks by the foreman. Not surprising when it could take a week or more to make the complete mould, work which was undone in a very few minutes.

Having picked up the broad outline of shaping metal by moulding and casting, I next went on to joining pieces together by welding. There was usually one 'Priv' in the welding shop, and he usually had one month there. Occasionally, one landed a three month stint, which, with hindsight, was a waste of time, because what you did learn could certainly be covered in four weeks, and the remaining eight did no more than enable one to improve technique and finish. I should point out that it was all electric welding, although I was able to persuade the supervising welder to let me have a go at some brazing of cast iron. We never did much 'useful' welding, and most of the time was spent joining cropped pieces of steel about 5 in. x 3 in. x ¼ in. or 5⁄16 in. thick, or perhaps putting down runs to leave one's initials on the bench for posterity.

After the welding shop came one of the best bits of my apprenticeship, with a spell at the running shed. I spent the first weeks with one of the fitters who concentrated on injector problems. A lot of the work was simply removing cones, and cleaning them, or maybe re-seating clack valves. I soon got to know about all the various bits which went into an exhaust injector, as well. At times, when we were short handed, I would be put to work on my own, but only on simple things (usually dirty as well) like taking up slack in brakes, or dealing with a leaking clack valve - much different when the engine is in steam. The normal form was to put the injector on, fill the boiler to the 'top nut' (on the gauge glass) and then clout the offending clack until the valve seated. The engine would then go off on a job and the unsuspecting crew would only find their problem when on the road. However, as the alternative was to drop the fire and take the engine 'out-of-steam' this was the normal procedure, until the next wash-out, when the valve could be properly dealt with.

After three weeks I went with the 'outside gang' who used the 40 ton steam breakdown crane for jobs which could not be handled in the shed, mainly hot axleboxes, where we lifted the engine to remove the offending wheels and axleboxes, which were sent into the works for attention. Usually, only the boxes went, although occasionally the journals were scored more than could be dealt with by use of emery cloth and had to be machined and polished. My time at the shed coincided with the works holidays and the favourite resort for Derby railway families must have been Great Yarmouth as, on the three Saturdays, there were usually five or six trains setting off for that destination, on the third one usually empty stock to bring them back! These trains were usually 10 or 11 coaches and invariably hauled by 'Big Goods', the LMS '4F'. The gang used to note the numbers on a blackboard and place bets on which would be 'on the pit' for leading axle hot-boxes the following Monday. While I was there, there were two on each of the three Mondays, and it then became a point of honour that we had them back together ready for the next weekend. There was certainly one that I remember was 'on the pit' on two successive Mondays, but I have not got a note of its number. The reason for the use of 'Big Goods' was the route, which was via the M&GN and restricted the size of locomotive which could be employed.

While at the shed, I was attached to the breakdown gang when they were called out. Being on the phone at home this meant that on one or two occasions, I was first on the train, even though I had to walk 2½ miles from home. This was fine, because you got paid from the minute you clocked on! I suppose I went to about a score of incidents, two of which were quite spectacular, one involving a run-away of coal wagons which piled up in a bridge arch at Bagworth, while the other was at Polesworth on 21st July, 1947 where a Euston-Liverpool express became derailed at speed, causing five fatalities. As our breakdown train set off, we were in danger of causing an incident ourselves, as our driver behaved as if he was going to a fire, and had us going well over 60 mph with everyone hanging out of the windows trying to attract his attention, and remind him we were limited to 45! Jobs like this involved working on and on until the track was clear, and at Polesworth, I saw the clock round twice, and a fair slice of a third time before I got home again. That week's work produced more than a fortnight's wages!

I was sorry when my stint at 4 Shed finished and I had to go back into the shops, but all good things come to an end sometime, and I also knew that I was now starting on the final phase of my apprenticeship, which would be spent in the erecting shop. As it turned out, I went to the bogie shop which as its name suggests dealt with repairs to bogies and ponytrucks which were built up and then taken complete to the erecting shop. As with most places, the bogie shop had its 'characters', one of these was the fellow who fitted axleguards to the bogies and trucks. He had two enormous tool boxes absolutely crammed with spanners, there must have been hundreds, and the boxes he kept tightly locked. He was slightly mental, and it was not unknown for him to start filing the rails to get the right distance from the guard to the rail, instead of marking the guard and having it burnt off! It may sound a tall story but 'tis true.

After bogies, I was back in the main erecting shop and had a spell on regulators, bedding the valve to its face, packing the stuffing box, fitting the handle to the rod, and closing the dome after ensuring that the cap was going to make a steam tight seal. A lot of this work was on boilers still on the frames, and it was quite a precarious perch on the curved barrel, trying to file or scrape the vertical face, while working down through the dome opening, or maybe swinging a lead hammer to tighten the nuts holding the cover down.

Valving was another section where I spent some time, with a mate called 'Nodder' because of a sort of nervous twitch that he had. My first day with him started by my being taken down into the 'vaults' to be introduced by the chargehand, Frank 'Nigger'* Wilson. Introductions over, I was invited by Nodder to take his tool bag to the '4F' we were to work on. When I tried to lift the bag, I nearly fell over! It weighed about a hundredweight, and I got used to humping it around. I investigated the contents, and found numerous spanners, chisels, hammers and no fewer than four lead hammers! I managed to dispose of two of these which eased my load a little.

'Nodder' was a good mate, and I learnt a lot about setting valves, 'jumping' or drawing out eccentric rods to make adjustments, and other tricks of the trade. Some of it was heavy work, like putting up the high pressure connecting rod on a Compound, or the inside rod on a 3-cylinder Stanier 2-6-4 tank. I also had to bar the wheels round on some engines, and I particularly remember that with the 6 ft 9 in. 4-4-0, care was necessary as one minute you were struggling to turn the wheel and the next it was 'over the top' and likely to take charge!

The 'plum' job in the erecting shop was new work, one of the big attractions being that it was cleaner than the repair work. I had a spell here too, when class '5' 4-6-0 engines were being built, and I worked on the smokeboxes, fitting steam pipes, packing the 'glands' through which the steampipes passed to reach

* Frank Wilson's nickname was perfectly acceptable at the time and he was quite happy with it, and responded to it. It was used by all, except the management, who would call him just Wilson. He was a big white man, very strong, and was said to be 'able to do the work of two men in half the time' and of 'working like a nigger', a phrase which was widely used in those days.

Derby No. 8 erecting shop in 1936 with newly-built 2-6-4T No. 2447 and partially constructed No. 2448 frames can be seen for the next. In the middle road, there appears to be a steam breakdown crane. *Author's Collection*

the cylinders, aligning the chimney and blastpipe and fitting the door to ensure an air-tight seal. The mate I had, Wilf Shrigley, was very helpful and sort of 'passed me round' some of the other erectors so that I got some insight into other aspects of building a new locomotive.

In due time came my 21st birthday, and I became a fully-fledged locomotive erector literally overnight. To make my joy complete, because, at this momentous time, I was working for Frank Wilson on valving, this meant that that was where I would ply my trade. Now, Frank did not like 'Privs' and had made that clear on my first spell with him; he persevered in his views despite my becoming a man! 'Right', says he on being told that my status had changed, 'let's find out what you have learned in the past few years'. He disappeared into his little cabin to consult his papers and came out again to say that he would find me a mate and that my first job would be to set up the rods and motion on a Compound!

Fortunately, when I was with 'Nodder', we had done a couple of these so I had a vague idea of what was involved. My mate, an apprentice fitter, and I went off to the tool stores to collect a set of tools against the requisition chit provided by Frank, and then we went off to find the Compound. We also had a labourer who would turn the wheels for us with a suitable wooden lever. A Compound was quite a difficult job with three sets of Stephenson gear and the crank for the high pressure connecting rod and its associated big end between the frames. After much grunting, sweating and so on, and some adjustment of valve rods in the smithy, we got it all together and 'boxed up' with steam chest covers in place. I was satisfied that the valves were set according to the set of gauges borrowed from the tool stores. To be fair to Frank, he turned up quite frequently to see how we were progressing and each time suggested how we should proceed. I think we went a piece over the time allocated to the task, but there was no come-back after the engine had gone to 4 Shed for trials, so it must have worked.

4-4-0 Compound No. 40936 in ex-works condition, sporting the early British Railways passenger livery, black with full lining out, on the test line, Derby No. 4 shed. On completing my apprenticeship and on my 21st birthday, my first job as an erector was to fit and set up the motion and valve gear on one of these engines. *Author*

So I had to go back to the cabin for our next job, and Frank seemed to grin malevolently as he said 'I've saved you a Tilbury', and gave me the number of one of the Stanier three-cylinder 2-6-4T locomotives which were the backbone of the service on the London, Tilbury & Southend lines out of Fenchurch Street. Whilst there was only one set of motion between the frames, together with the crank, the inside connecting rod was a monster and a real pig of a job to erect. In due course, I was able to report that it was complete, and Frank had the decency to say that I had made a good job of my first days as a valver.

From then on he did not give me another three-cylinder job, and it was 'Big Goods', class '2P' 4-4-0, a 'Jinty', '3F' 0-6-0, and 2-6-2 and 2-6-4 tanks. I definitely preferred the last two types, as everything was on the outside!

Then, one morning, Frank said that he had had a note to the effect that, come the following Monday, I was to report to the planning engineer. 'So you're on your way' was how he put it. It marked the end of my training as a locomotive engineer, and I went home that afternoon wondering what the future would hold.

While proof-testing Shrewsbury steam crane No. RS10/30, things got out of hand on 7th April, 1949. A shot from the staff footbridge at Derby has caught the works manager, Tom Simpson, eyeballing the author as his deputy, Maurice Henstock, approaches from the left. I half-expected to be 'on the carpet' but he must not have recognised me!

Author's Collection

Chapter Three

I Join the Drawing Office Staff

Monday morning dawned and, despite the fact that this was the day I was to go 'up the Offices' as Frank Wilson put it, the routine was little different from all the preceding days through my apprenticeship. I still had to get my breakfast and then leg it to the bus stop to catch the works bus, run by the local bus company. But there was a difference - I was turned out in jacket and tie, which caused a few comments on the bus. 'No more overalls then.' 'Gone upstairs then, have we?' and the like. There was another advantage, too, inasmuch as I no longer had to 'clock on', which, on occasions when the bus was delayed, had meant that I had had to sprint through the works to reach my time clock to record my arrival time. There was a two minute allowance after the prescribed time, but, if you missed out, even a single minute lost you a quarter-hour's pay. In the offices, you signed a book and wrote down your arrival time. Mind you, questions were asked if you noted down a time which was earlier than that against the previous signature!

So it was that I found my way into the planning office on the appointed morning, and had to hang about until the planning engineer turned up at nine o'clock to give me my instructions. There were several other early starters, mainly progressmen who I already knew, so I found myself in good company. My duties started off with 'catalogue reprint', which was an on-going job whereby the Locomotive Stores Department catalogue of parts was being worked through to check that the description of stores items tied up with what was on the shelf, and also to remove any duplication, of which I came across quite a few. I think there were four of us on this checking, and it involved a lot of leg-work, but it was to stand me in good stead later as I became familiar with the stores procedure, and the staff concerned.

After a stint on this for about three months, I was put to tracing out-of-date stock orders, which basically meant that I had to make certain that the items had been made, and were either still in stock or had been used. Some of these orders were umpteen years old, and tracing them was quite a job. One which sticks in my memory was for a number, I think 20, of chimneys for 'Royal Scot' locomotives, which was issued in 1933 or 1934. As the order in my hand was then 15 years old, and as I could not find a pile of castings - we were rebuilding 'Royal Scots' in 1948 anyway with double chimneys - I scrawled across the order 'All stock issued', although I hardly think that the original 'Royal Scots' wore out chimneys at that rate! Anyway, it must have satisfied somebody, because it was never queried!

Having just started on this job, I was asked if I would stand in for one of my colleagues who was helping with the Locomotive Interchange Trials. George had booked his holidays before he was asked to participate in these tests, and it sounded an attractive proposition. I was to be at Toton shed and my job was to supervise the loading of coal on to the test locomotive out of a wagon which had already been weighed, and which was weighed again after the tender had been

Ex-SR 'West Country' class 4-6-2 No. 34005 *Barnstaple* with LMS tender stands at No. 6 platform, Derby Midland with the Manchester to St Pancras train on 25th June, 1948, during the Locomotive Interchanges. The first vehicle in the train is No. 1 Dynamometer Car. *Author*

A locomotive which had an immense impact on the direction my railway career took, British Railways Eastern Region 'O1' class 2-8-0 No. 63789 at Toton during the Interchange trials on 21st July, 1948. *Author*

filled to establish the amount of coal loaded. In the same way when the train arrived at the end of a test run, all remaining coal in the tender was transferred to a pre-weighed empty wagon, subsequent weighing establishing the residual amount at the end of the run, and by subtracting this from the coal loaded prior to the run, gave the coal burnt during the test run. A separate supply was arranged for preparation and light running. I had a most enjoyable time at Toton during the period that the ex-London & North Eastern Railway (LNER) 'O1' 2-8-0 No. 63789 was running between Toton and Brent. The work was quite leisurely, although there was a lot of hanging about awaiting arrival, due to loss of time on the journey. The LMS No. 1 Dynamometer Car was used on these trains and I got to know the team of technicians, treating them with the awe and deference obviously due to them. I was even allowed into the car, given a cup of tea and had the mass of intricate recording equipment explained to me. Again, as with the job involving the stores, I had no idea what this little diversion with No. 63789 was going to lead to; in fact, it was to be a significant factor in the direction my future railway career was to take.

Like all good things which come to an end, my time at Toton was soon over and I went back to my stock orders, relieved briefly by my own holiday, and then on through the autumn until one day in mid-November I was sent for by the planning engineer and asked if I would be interested in going to the drawing office for four weeks 'to assist with the analysis of the Interchange records'. It seems that Vic Roberts, who was in charge of the dynamometer car, had 'made a note of my name' in July, and had now suggested that I might be invited to help. Needless to say, I took no time to make up my mind, and the following Monday I presented myself at the Holy of Holies, along with Basil Watson who you will remember had the ignominious lift out of the boiler described previously, and who had also agreed to help with the analysis, although he had not been involved in any way with the tests themselves. It was quite a change to be working 'office' hours, although at that time it still involved working two Saturdays in three, for three hours in the morning.

The work Baz and I were set to do was to go through the dynamometer charts, and for a particular test stretch, count up the Work Done peaks. The dynamometer combined speed of the train and drawbar pull in a simple integrator. This was in the form of a horizontal brass disc with a polished surface, which was driven by the road wheel, this being an additional wheel on one bogie between the two carrying axles at one side, and capable of being lowered on to the rail from inside the vehicle. This meant that the faster the train went, the faster the disc rotated. Resting on the face of the disc was a wheel, standing vertically and having a chamfer on each side to give a narrow rim in contact with the disc. This wheel was carried on a spindle made in the form of a very long pinion, which could slide past a gear wheel in mesh with it, the spindle being carried on a carriage which was moved horizontally in proportion to the pull on the drawbar. So you can see that as the wheel moved across the disc away from the centre of the latter, it would turn, and the greater the distance it moved sideways, the faster it would go round (assuming a constant rotational speed of the disc).

This means in effect that the greater the work done by the locomotive, the faster will the vertical wheel rotate and, in rotating, it drove through gears a

No.1 Dynamometer Car No. 45050. Originally built by the Lancashire & Yorkshire Railway at Horwich works in 1912. *Author's Collection*

heart shaped cam which in its turn moved a recording pen backwards and forwards across a portion of the recorder roll. As the paper moved across the recording table in proportion to train speed (driven from the road wheel) the movement of the pen produced a saw tooth series of peaks, close together at high power outputs, and more spaced out as power was reduced, being a horizontal line when the train was coasting. In this condition, although the disc is turning, the drawbar pull is zero and hence the wheel is at the centre of the disc so is not rotating, and there is no cam movement.

Having diverted myself into the intricacies of the dynamometer car, perhaps it would be better if I spent some time in describing the rest of the vehicle The No. 1 Dynamometer Car was built for the Lancashire & Yorkshire Railway (L&Y) in 1913 to the design of George Hughes, the CME. The drawbar pull was taken by a series of single-leaf springs, coupled by links, in such a way that the overall stiffness could be varied, although throughout my association with the vehicle I cannot recall an occasion when we ever used other than the full assembly. There was also a smaller group of similar springs which came into operation under buffing conditions.

In a way, the vehicle was a mobile spring balance with trimmings. As mentioned earlier, the speed of its mobility was measured by means of a 'road wheel', turned to an accurate diameter to give a precise number of revolutions per mile and used to drive a speedometer, and also to power the recording table. The latter was the most obvious feature in the main saloon in the car, and had a heavy cast-iron top which carried the recording paper and the various pens which recorded speed, drawbar pull, the integrated work saw-tooth already mentioned, a seconds line for accurate time assessment, a minutes line to avoid the need for counting up the seconds pulses, a distance line which I think marked every mile covered, and an event line which responded to bell pushes placed at strategic points so that features like tunnels, stations and the like could be marked on the chart. The chart movement, being driven from the road wheel, moved in proportion to vehicle speed, so that the faster the train went, the faster the paper moved across the table.

The recording pens used ordinary fountain pen ink and were a source of constant trouble. We used blue, green, red and purple, the ink being loaded into the body of the pen with an eye-dropper type of feeder. The pen was a brass tube with a push-in tip into which was soldered a length of hypodermic needle. In use, the pens tended to blot, or run dry or even dig into and tear the paper and constant surveillance of the table was essential, with at least as many pens in reserve as were in operation. It called for an operator to watch and change the pens and a junior (me!) to take away faulty pens, unblock and refill and return them during test runs. Although I am jumping ahead in time, to the period when I was a member of the team, it became my job in due course to look after the pens and service them between test series. I was able to improve matters to a considerable degree by fitting the whole lot with new hypodermic tubes (I remember buying two three-foot lengths from Accles and Pollock, the sort of name you never forget, once you have heard it!) and then very carefully squaring the end on a slip stone and finally even more carefully stoning off the sharp edge using a magnifying glass to assess progress. I also did some experimenting on my own account with the inks and found we had most blots with red ink, although those pens rarely ran

Interior of No. 1 Dynamometer Car with the recording table in the foreground. In the background can be seen the observation window at the front of the vehicle with the two seats and the raised platform between them. The large double-faced speedometer referred to opposite can be seen above the left-hand side of the recording table.

dry while the other three colours more often blocked the pens. I did some filtering tests and found that the red ink just coloured a filter paper but the blue, green and purple while colouring the paper left a much darker mark near the centre. Re-running the filtered ink resulted in a much more even colouring. So I prepared quantities of filtered ink ready for the next series of tests without saying anything and was gratified when after a couple of runs Ronnie Woore who was the 'table-minder' said to me 'Young Rimmer' (he came from a wealthy family and only later did he start to use my Christian name, although I was allowed to call him Ron after a short time - Mr Woore at first though), 'Young Rimmer', he said, 'I don't know what you have been up to, but these pens are working better than I have known them to for a long time. Keep it up'. I did not let on until it was obvious that there had been a real improvement, just kept quietly filtering the ink. I got over the 'red' problem too by changing the make - I think I changed to Stephens from Watermans, but it could well have been vice versa.

Now back to my description of the car - hope the diversion was of interest. There was a second table in the main saloon, about the size of a small dining table, and at which the deputy section leader usually sat to work out spot checks during the test, such as drawbar horse power over a one-minute period or the like. The chief, Vic Roberts, was an Organiser with a capital 'O', while his deputy, Ernest Sharp, was shall we say the Academic. It was Ernest who wielded the slide rule and worked out results both during and after the runs, while Vic wrote up the report to incorporate Ernest's figures and also got on organising the next series of tests. The table also carried a large double-faced speedometer that anyone virtually anywhere in the saloon could see the speed the train was travelling. At the front end of the saloon there were two steps up to a platform at each side of which were single comfortable seats fronted by a large window which went right up to the curve of the roof, and enabled one to see over the tender of some locomotives into the cab, although with the Stanier tender this was not possible. In front of one seat was a rack with pieces of board with figures like 30, 35, 40, etc., which could be held up to tell the footplate crew how fast they were going. Also a 'plus' sign which meant 'go faster' and a 'minus' sign which was 'slow down'.

The remainder of the car was taken up by, going rearwards from the saloon, a first class compartment, used for visitors, or for conferences with VIP's during tests (and as we shall see later for 'messing'). Then there was a compartment with a coal-fired stove, again about which more later, a toilet cum wash room, and finally a vestibule with cupboards for tools, teapots, cups, plates, cutlery and all the vital impedimenta so essential for the smooth running of a vehicle of this nature.

So there you have it, a brief description of the vehicle which, when invited to step inside at Toton, I entered as if it was the Holy of Holies, peopled by genii. Before I started its description, Baz and I had just been selected, on a temporary basis, to help with assessment and analysis of the Interchange records. Let us now proceed.

The work lasted for about five weeks and took us to within a week of Christmas 1948. Vic Roberts asked the head of the drawing office, a formidable fellow called Tom Coleman who had only to come into the drawing office and stand and glower down its length to have every pencil hard at work, whether

Interior of No. 1 Dynamometer Car looking at the recording table and the side corridor leading to the rear vestibule. *Author's Collection*

Interior of No. 1 Dynamometer Car with Pat Webb, *top left*, and then clockwise; Alan Saunders, Cliff Belfield, Walter King and Ernest Sharp. *Author*

we should be sent back whence we came. Mr Coleman replied that surely Vic could find us some work to do for a time, which was really an order. So it was that we were put to sorting out a storeroom full of old drawings and all sorts of bits and pieces which the test section had accumulated. A couple of drawings I remember well were linen-mounted prints of *The Great Bear,* a general arrangement which would have been about 7¼ in. gauge, and the associated valve gear at a larger scale; odd things to find at Derby indeed. After the cupboard, we then started on a mass of tracings in about five big drawers. Some of these were really fascinating as they were engine diagrams for 'might-have-beens'. Such as a 2-6-2 version of the rebuilt 'Scot' (Derby answer to the 'V2'), various 0-6-0 tender engines with bar frames, outside cylinders and other ideas obviously replacements for the '4F', a 2-8-4T made by grafting tanks and a bunker on to a Stanier '8F', and many, many more. How I wish now that I had been able to have got copies of all of these. There were a vast variety, I seem to remember a 4-8-2 passenger engine and a dainty little 2-4-2T rather like the large boilered Stanier '3P' tank of which our local example was No. 169 shedded at Rowsley. There was certainly plenty of choice for the small locomotive man who wanted to be just that bit different and yet know he was in effect treading a path pointed out in full size.

In due time, all the tracings were sorted and stored away (I wonder where they are now?) and still Mr Coleman would not let Vic send us back - not that we were pressing, mind you! 'Find them a job, Roberts. Surely you can make good use of them can't you'. And so it was that we were found a permanent place in the drawing office, at the end of the long row of boards down one side, right outside the chief draughtsman's office and across from the partitioned off sanctum housing Vic Roberts, Ernest Sharp and a fellow called Vic Stockton. The latter was a real 'character' and a brilliant artist. He it was who was responsible for the 'exploded' sketches, isometric drawings of, say, the front end of a 'Coronation' Pacific, or for colouring a General Arrangement. He was a wizard with an air-brush - this in 1948 - and like many artists, for such he undoubtedly was, he was shall we say an individual and I found him a very interesting and colourful character. He felt he was grossly underpaid for his work and talents and various cryptic cartoons and statements around the walls made this plain for all to see.

Now that we were established, Vic had to find us work to do. We were given graphs to plot and other work on the periphery of the Interchange Trials, which were going to occupy many weeks of work and which precluded any other running tests being undertaken, although of course, there was a fair amount of design activity going on, with talk of Standard Engines and for which the results of the trials would provide valuable information.

Baz and I were both given some drawing work to do, although as we only had one board between us, one of us was always occupied on something else. One incident I recall clearly involved Baz (of course). The LMS, as well as the LNER, had trouble with inside big ends. On the 'A4s', a capsule was fitted which, when it got hot, emitted a strong smell of violets, which the driver was more or less bound to notice, enabling him to slow his train and probably limit any major damage. This was fairly well known, but what was possibly less well known that similar problems beset the 'Jubilees' at one time and certain engines

Interior of No. 1 Dynamometer Car with Ian Hunter on the left, Ernest Sharp on the right, Vic Roberts behind the speedometer, then Walter King, Cliff Belfield and Alan Saunders. *Author*

Interior of No. 1 Dynamometer Car with Ernest Sharp in the foreground, Walter King behind him, Cliff Belfield with the earphones, Alan Saunders behind the table and Pat Webb on the left. *Author*

were fitted with a similar capsule. This was a length of tube with plugs brazed into the ends, one plug having a taper thread for a smaller plug which had cross-drilled holes and an axial hole from the cross holes towards the tube, the cross holes being sealed with a low melting point alloy called Cerrobend. The capsule was filled with a chemical called Butyl Mercaptan which smelt of anything but violets! It was foul and might be likened to the concentrated aroma of a filthy farmyard on a hot summer day. The testing section was the custodian of this chemical which was kept in a flask with a neck sealed by melting the glass. One day, Basil had to take the flask and a capsule to the Research Department chemistry lab next door for the capsule to be filled and the flask resealed. In some way, he made the flask leak so that it dripped a trail of drops as he walked down the office, making the place uninhabitable until all the windows were opened and the stink cleared. Baz was all innocence when he came back, and had 'no idea' the flask was leaking. From then on Vic kept the flask in his sanctum, instead of in the cupboard behind our board.

As I said, we were given quite a few 'little' jobs of an experimental nature and very often left to our own devices. One which came my way was to investigate the burning in a guard's (oil) handlamp which tended to be uneven. With half a dozen of the oil containers and wick-holders, I found that there was a tendency for the flame to become larger as the oil level dropped, without any alteration being made to the wick. It did not seem to be affected by the age of the equipment, both new and old assemblies behaving in the same manner.

I concluded that it might be caused by the air which was in the container being affected by the heat and exerting just enough pressure to feed oil slightly faster, although as the oil was consumed, air had to find its way in round the wick assembly, so there should not have been any pressure build-up. Whatever the cause, I was expected to provide a solution! I decided to try filling the container with cotton wool for a start, and Eureka! it worked. The flame would remain stable until it went out through oil starvation, and the cotton wool was only slightly 'damp' with oil. One side effect was that the burning time was increased by about 18 to 20 per cent but the most remarkable effect I found was that by packing the container with cotton wool, it took about 7 to 8 per cent more oil to fill it than when there was no cotton wool in it! At first I thought I had made a mistake, but after checking carefully, and getting Ernest to watch what I did, he vertified that I was right. He was as mystified as I was, and even when the container was packed really tightly with cotton wool, it would still hold the same amount of oil. The scientific chaps in the Research Department next door were approached and they too confirmed the phenomenon, but could not come up with an explanation. As far as I know, there was no bulk order placed for cotton wool and guards' handlamps continued to be used as before, i.e. they either burned with a bigger, usually smoky, flame or the guard adjusted the wick! But I still wonder what happened to give the effect that I found.

EX-WD 0-6-0T, LMS 'Jinty' No. 7607 on arrival at Derby after repatriation from France on 4th October, 1948. *Author*

A new 2-6-4T hanging from the cranes and ready to be lowered onto its wheels. Taken when posed for the artist Terence Cuneo in April 1949. *Author*

Chapter Four

Some Memories of Locomotive Testing

In the 'limbo' period following the Interchange trials in 1948, and my contribution in the early stages of the analysis, and having been, at least temporarily, attached to the Locomotive Testing Section, one of the most interesting activities which was going on was the completion of the LMS No. 3 Dynamometer Car. Prior to World War II, the LMS Railway had designed and started building, in 1936, this vehicle and three mobile testing units which were to form a train by means of which controlled road tests could be carried out, and which would be complementary to work carried out in the Locomotive Testing Plant built at Rugby as a joint venture by the LMS and LNER. It should not be thought, however, that a series of tests would always be carried out on both facilities, as trials either on the plant, or on the road, were capable of standing complete in their own right.

However, tests on the stationary plant completely removed the effect of weather and other variables. The difficulty with road tests was to cater for changes in gradient, particularly from rising to falling which of course normally produced an increase of speed, and the mobile test plant was designed to cope with such changes, being capable of maintaining a constant speed up hill and down dale provided the locomotive was working hard enough to lift the train up the gradients. This meant that it was possible to approach the constant conditions so readily achievable 'indoors' on the plant, when out on the normal railway.

The mobile test units had been virtually completed by the outbreak of the war, but the dynamometer car had some work outstanding. The whole project was shelved during the period of hostilities, and had been 'dusted off' in late 1948. So in the early months of 1949, I made several visits into the carriage and wagon works at Derby to see the progress on the new vehicle. By comparison with the old No. 1 car, it was much improved, with a hydraulic dynamometer and a very sophisticated recording table, one of the most notable features of which was the array of four large steel balls (about 4 in. diameter) which formed the integrating equipment for producing drawbar horse power, speed, work done at the drawbar and work done against acceleration and gradient. In the last case, where the train was controlled by the mobile test units to run at constant speed, then a direct measurement of gradient was produced. The basis for this measurement was a large, heavily damped pendulum suspended beneath the recording table.

The recording table, as with the old L&Y car, had a continuous paper roll on which the data was recorded. This could be fed either at constant speed from an electric motor drive, or proportionately to distance by taking the drive from the road wheel. In both cases, a choice of three rates of advance was available through a gear box.

There was a large array of recording pens dealing with basic functions like drawbar pull, speed, drawbar horsepower, and work done. Additionally, intervals of time in seconds and minutes showed on two traces, while pens operated by remote push buttons could mark stations, mileposts, tunnels, etc., bags of coal burnt and safety valve opening, these latter two being from the observer on the footplate, while water consumption to the injectors was metered and contacts within the Kent flowmeter showed on the chart, if my memory is correct, every 25 gallons. I should point out that the mobile test plant included a special tender which was fitted with this water meter, and also had a through corridor so that dynamometer car staff could reach the footplate during a test. Two separate compartments were provided for coal, one for loose coal, and one for bagged, pre-weighed coal. The tender had a steam winch on top behind the coal space, and a crane jib which fitted into a socket, and by this means the bags of coal could be dragged up a slide which rested against the tender side to facilitate loading. Steam for the winch engine came from the carriage heating supply pipe.

Before we leave the mobile test plant, I should perhaps mention that the dynamometer car would later include a gas analysis panel to examine smoke box gases, a Farnborough indicator for taking indicator diagrams from which indicated drawbar horsepower could be calculated, and recording equipment associated with the weighing grate, which was designed to give a continuous reading of the weight of the grate and the fire thereon, and was intended to be used to try to finish a test sequence with approximately the same weight of fire as at the beginning. This was essential if tests were of relatively short duration, say 30 or 40 minutes, because if the fire thickness was only an inch or two different, this was virtually impossible to judge by eye - and even the use of a pricker with a right angled strip welded to it, which was poked down through the fire to the bars was not a lot of help - then the coal consumption figure could be rather wide of the mark. If coal was burnt off to give a thinner fire, then a good figure would ensue, while if there was more coal on the grate than when the test started, the engine would be discredited as having an excessive coal consumption and hence a poor evaporation rate.

I shall come back later in the book to talk about the Farnborough indicator, which I learnt to operate, and also the weighing grate, with which I also became closely associated for a time. Meanwhile, having been paying regular visits to the carriage and wagon works to see the progress towards finishing off Dynamometer Car No. 3 and becoming familiar with, in particular, its recording facilities, I became imbued with the underlying sense of excitement which was running through the whole section as the time came nearer when we were going to take the whole mobile test plant out on the road for the first time.

In due course, it was sufficiently complete for initial trials to begin and the whole entourage was moved to Rugby which became a base from which trials were carried out. In those days the lines to Leicester and to Peterborough were open and both of these were used for trials, which were to test out the equipment and prove it, and make any necessary adjustments. As far as I recall, we did not use the tender in these earlier stages, but all the rest of it was in use. One of the more spectacular tests was the shock-load test, which was to prove that the electronic control systems on the mobile test units could cope with large changes of drawbar pull without the speed varying widely. To do this, the train was run between Rugby and Willesden and back, and was double-headed by an LMS Compound 4-4-0 No. 41080 and an ex-Southern Railway 'Merchant Navy' class Pacific, the scheme being that the Compound would haul the train most of the time, and the mobile test units would be set to a particular speed, ready for the load to be applied. The 'Merchant Navy' was used to apply the shock load by opening the regulator wide while running in mid-gear until, at a given signal, the steam-reverser was dropped into full forward gear. The sound effects in the train were fantastic! First of all the sudden roar of exhaust, followed seconds afterwards by the rattle of the coal on the dynamometer car roof! I'm sure that on occasions, there must have been firebars as well! The load was only kept on for a minute or so, and then the regulator was closed on the 4-6-2 and the fireman went to work to re-build the fire, re-fill the boiler and bring the pressure back, ready for the next trial. It usually took between 15 and 20 minutes before a repeat could be attempted, but the whole exercise was very informative, and proved that the control systems were able to cope extremely well, with no significant change in speed.

With the major commissioning of the test plant completed, an opportunity had been arranged to demonstrate its capabilities to the Institution of Locomotive Engineers, as part of their Summer Meeting in 1949. This took place between the 10th and 13th May and commenced with a visit to the Locomotive Testing Station at Rugby, which, incidentally to our trials with the mobile plant, I was getting to know quite well, along with members of the staff. The Testing Station recording table was very similar to that in the dynamometer car, although there was no acceleration / gradient record made, for obvious reasons!

After visiting the Testing Station, the members attending the meeting joined a special train made up of Dynamometer Car No. 3, a kitchen car and eight vestibule carriages, and hauled by class '5' 4-6-0 No. 4752 which was built in March of the previous year and was one of a batch fitted with Caprotti valve gear and Timken roller bearings.

The train left Rugby at 4.30 pm, and tea was served during the journey to Manchester. My role on this day was assistant at the recording table, and most of my time was fully occupied with keeping the pens running, and marking up the chart, as my senior colleague was involved in explaining the technicalities to the visitors who came into the car in small groups. The train was easily timed, so that there was nothing particularly notable about the run and we reached Manchester London Road (now Piccadilly) in a little over two hours. After the visitors had left, the train moved out to Longsight, and we found our way to the enginemen's hostel where accommodation had been arranged for us.

These hostels or 'barracks' as they were sometimes called, were mainly used by engine crews on lodging turns, where they would work away from their home station, stay in the hostel and work back the next day. The practice has long since ceased but at one time, 'lodging jobs' were accepted as a regular part of life by many train crews. I remember reading a book *Speeding North with the Royal Scot* written by Laurie Earl in which he recounts his experiences, which included 'lodging' in Glasgow, having driven from Euston, and in which two round trips formed a week's work, just four days! I think this was probably one of the longer jobs, but Birmingham-Glasgow, Liverpool and Manchester to

The footplate of 'Jubilee' class No. 45699 *Galatea* in all its pristine glory, all highly polished on the occasion of the Institution of Locomotive Engineers summer meeting demonstration run from Manchester Central to Derby, 13th May, 1949.
Author

London, Toton-Cricklewood, and many, many others formed part of the pattern of life in the 1940s and 1950s.

I came to know, and enjoy, the life in these places, which varied considerably in the standards they achieved. Longsight was not my first hostel, as we had stayed in the one at Rugby while doing the trials described earlier, and Rugby to my mind was always bottom of the league. It was always clean, but there was not much else you could say for it! Built at the back of the engine shed, it really was a 'barracks' with the sleeping accommodation formed by wooden partitions down each side of a large room, the partitions stopping about six inches above the floor, standing about six and a half feet high and failing to reach the ceiling by about two feet. This made the 'dormitories' noisy, as men would be coming in and going out all through the night, often being called by the clerk in charge, who was not bothered about how many others he woke, and of course, if anyone snored, it was diabolical!

Many of the ex-London & North Western Railway (LNWR) hostels were similar, but had been 'modernised' with full length partitions, which was a big improvement. Some that I was to come across, like Camden and Upperby (Carlisle) were more modern and had separate cubicles. In fact, I believe that the Upperby hostel is now part of a motel!

The Locomotive Engineers' Summer meeting next involved us on Friday, 13th May, and the dynamometer car had been worked from Longsight to Cornbrook Sidings on the Wednesday, and been united with Mobile Test Units Nos. 1 and 2. With the addition of three passenger carriages, the train stood in Manchester Central just before 9 am, headed by 'Jubilee' No. 45699 *Galatea*, which was in superb condition. I well remember the footplate had been given a lot of attention, with all the copper pipes and brassware gleaming, and the steelwork such as the regulator handle and reverser had been gone over with emery cloth and then wiped with an oily rag. I took a photograph at the time, but the combination of the difficulty of getting back far enough (up on front of the tender peering down under the cab roof), black and white film, and the lack of flash produced results which failed to do justice to the sight. How different it would be with modern equipment and film.

Although the train was light for a 'Jubilee' over Peak Forest, the use of the mobile test units enabled the effect of a much heavier train to be simulated and a very effective demonstration of the equipment was possible, again with parties of visitors continually being shepherded round the dynamometer car, with the run terminating at Derby, from where the visitors attending the meeting dispersed and we went back to the office!

Not for long, however. The following Monday found us back in No. 1 car and heading for Crewe, which was to be base for a series of tests on the ex-LMS Ivatt class '4' 2-6-0, the first of which, No. 3000, had appeared in 1947. Older readers may remember that these engines had an enormous double chimney as built, and they soon earned themselves a reputation as shy steamers. So it was that No. 43027 had been modified in Crewe works with a single chimney, according to my notes as fitted to a class '5' locomotive. We had a rake of empty coaching stock for our load and set off on the Tuesday morning for Holyhead. This was a line I knew to some extent, at least as far as Bangor, as

Ivatt class '4' No. 43027 at Holyhead on 24th May, 1949. The engine is fitted with the chimney and blastpipe from a class '4' 2-6-4 tank locomotive.

Author

we had been to Penmaenmawr for family holidays when I was a boy in the mid-1930s.

For these tests, we organised the weighing and loading of coal at Crewe and Holyhead with the supervisor (me) travelling on the train with the rest of the crew. As we did down and up journeys on successive days, there was plenty of time to see the loading after the run had been completed, ready for the following day. The first two days were run with a particular arrangement of chimney and blastpipe cap, and then two days with a different diameter of cap, and the whole programme was then completed with a chimney from a class '4' tank.

I was able on one of the down journeys to ride on the footplate of No. 43027 and it was a journey which I can still recall very vividly, particularly in certain aspects. Although these tests took place in May, this particular day was wet and very windy, and as we ran along the coast beyond Conway, the sea on our right was very rough, with huge waves breaking on the shore below. Across the Tubular Bridge and on to Anglesey and the wind seemed to be getting stronger, blowing directly on to the smokebox front, and whipping the exhaust away from the chimney top. We passed Valley into a full gale, and on to the causeway which connects with Holy Island on which Holyhead is built. Ahead of us, through the beating rain we could see two figures, permanent way men, trudging along with their heads down against the wind, in the 'four-foot' with their backs to us. A long blast on the whistle did not move them, and the driver slammed the brake on, they were about 50 yards away, and our howling whistle was obviously being blown away by the wind. The inspector came across to the driver, opened the cylinder cocks, and pushed the regulator open, and the two figures were hidden in a cloud of steam.

Peering over the cab side, I saw one man stumbling and waving his fist. Dan Drury - the inspector - saw the other fellow crossing the up line, so all was well, but it must have been a close thing. Dan reported it, and the men concerned were reprimanded, as they should not have been walking with their backs to traffic. I know my legs felt like jelly for quite a while after we reached Holyhead.

Talking about Dan Drury, who was based at Crewe, this was the first time I had met him. Over the years, I was to get to know Dan very well, and I was always ready to listen to him, particularly if he started to reminisce about the days when he was firing and driving. In the evening of the day when we had the near-miss described above, we were gathered round a blazing fire in the messroom of the Holyhead hostel and Dan was telling us about some of his exploits on the 'Corridor'. He had started as a cleaner at Crewe North in LNWR days, and worked his way up as fireman, passed fireman and driver, and had a tremendous fund of tales to tell, many of which I heard several times, but all of which lost nothing for having been repeated!

The hostel at Holyhead was a marked contrast to that at Rugby where I had been only a few days earlier. Although it had the same dormitory arrangements, it was as clean as a new pin, probably because it was looked after by a lady! Mrs Jones - who else in North Wales - supervised everything and always seemed to be there, from when we came down for breakfast in the morning, until late at night, when we would come in after having been out for a meal in the town, usually washed down with a few glasses. As soon as we came in, a plate of sandwiches appeared together with a big pot of tea, and woe betide us if we did not clear the plate! Looking back, I suppose that Holyhead was probably the best of all the hostels I ever stayed in, certainly the most homely, and just that little bit better than even Upperby and Kingmoor, which were the most modern and therefore had much better sleeping, washing and recreational facilities.

This test series seemed to fly by, and most enjoyable they were too. Before we leave them, one other little thing that impressed itself on me comes to mind. At that time, there was a permanent speed restriction of 30 mph on the sharp curve through Conway station and I was fascinated to see how the speedometer in the dynamometer car indicated exactly that speed every time, even with different drivers at the regulator, and despite the fact that there was not any speed indicator on the engine. When I asked Dan what the secret was, he said it was just the driver's judgment. I still don't understand how he got the judgment in the first place.

Following these tests, we had about five weeks in the office, analysing the results and writing up the report, before we were off out again, this time to carry out a series of comparative tests on LMS class '5' engines, with different valve gear and smokebox arrangements. Four locomotives were involved, No. 44757 which was fitted with Caprotti valve gear, and a twin blast pipe with 3⅝ in. diameter nozzles; No. 44764 which had Walschaert gear, and a single blast pipe with 5⅛ in. diameter cap; No. 44766, again a Walschaert engine but with twin 3¾ in. blast pipe, and the unique No. 44767 with outside Stephenson valve gear and the same smokebox arrangement as on No. 44766.

The test series occupied four weeks in total, a week for each locomotive. The tests were conducted between London St Pancras and Manchester Central, and involved working normal service trains, the 10.15 am down one day and the 4.15 pm up the next, and then repeating the sequence. There was no attempt made to cover all the work with a special train crew, although an inspector rode on the footplate. Each locomotive was in fact handled by three sets of enginemen, one set on the first day (Tuesday), the second set then covered the next two days, and the final set brought the train back to London on Friday. In 1949, lodging turns were still in common practice, and these were all Trafford Park men, who lodged overnight at Kentish Town.

My contribution to the activities was as the 'anchor-man' of Kentish Town Depot, where I had to supervise the coaling of the tender in the same way as I had done at Toton. I also had preparation to do on 'next week's' engine. This really involved the tender, which had to be fitted with an air pipe running vertically downwards into the water space, and ending six inches from the sole plate. This was used in conjunction with a calibrated tube in the dynamometer car, air being pumped into the pipe and causing the level in the tube to rise until it corresponded with the level in the tender tank. Another job was involved here too. Starting with a full tender, the water was run off into a dustbin whose capacity had been measured and by noting the depth in the tank every 100 gallons or thereabouts on a big dip-stick, it was possible to plot a graph showing the relationship of water level and total water in the tank. In this way, the dynamometer car tube, in giving a depth-of-water reading enabled a chart to be consulted and hence the amount of water in the tank to be arrived at. By taking readings at regular intervals, water consumption was measured, to give an indication of the amount of steam being generated. There was no attempt made to measure losses such as injector overflow, although an eye was kept on this, and notes made if it became excessive, The continuous blow-down fitted to the locomotives was blanked off, and the water treated with Polyamide at the beginning of each run. There were of course water trough pick-ups and the water tank monitor had to use his gauge to make an assessment of the amount picked up each time.

The calibration of the tender was a slow, tedious, backbreaking and wet job. However, once the tender had been emptied, then the balance pipe could be fitted, which involved taking an oxy-acetylene burner into the tank to blow out a couple of rivets, so that the clamps securing the pipe could be secured. The effect of the burner in the confined space was to raise the humidity well above 100 per cent, so that after about three minutes you came out absolutely wringing wet through. Fortunately, it was July and August time, and being young and foolish (?) I just used to carry on working and let my clothes dry on me. It was usually afternoon anyway, so I was able to go to the Kentish Town 'Lodge' and have a bath when I had finished.

The times of the trains meant that on Monday, I had to get the tender filled with coal, and then once the locomotive and dynamometer car went off the shed on Tuesday morning at about 9.30, I did not see them until the following evening at about half past nine. I was then faced with organising the removal of the remainder of the coal, followed by supervising the best part of nine tons being hand loaded into the empty tender. A quantity was also piled on to the footplate for building up the fire which had been cleaned and damped down, so that coal was not taken out of the tender which would have affected the coal consumption calculations. It was well on to or even after dawn most mornings by the time I finished, went to the hostel, had a quick bath and then bed. Only for a short, time, because Vic Roberts still expected me to be there when they went off the shed. Having seen them go, I usually went to the little 'caf' down the road for some breakfast and then back to bed for a spell.

I managed to get a bit of time to myself, and I see from my notes that I went to places like New Cross, Neasden, and Stratford, obviously looking at Large Locomotives. I also ventured as far as Brighton one day, no doubt for the same reason, and I think it was on that occasion that I saw No. 36001, the only 'Leader' ever to be completed. I also had a trip to Southend, where a school friend lived, and we went watching the Tilbury tanks and the three-cylinder 2-6-4Ts that worked out of Fenchurch Street.

I suppose in a way my involvement seemed less with the class fives than with No. 43027, inasmuch as I did not ride on the trains at all. Nevertheless, I was enjoying myself and thanking my lucky stars that I had been available 12 months earlier to go to Toton, never dreaming at that time that it was going to lead on to this, just as I had very little inkling of the exciting events which would unfold as part of my Privileged View of Steam.

'Leader' class 0-6-6-0 No. 36001 outside Brighton works on 14th July, 1949. *Author*

Chapter Five

The Mobile Testing Plant

One of the class '5' locomotives which was tested between St Pancras and Manchester, No. 44764, which was the single chimney/blast pipe, Walschaert geared engine, was the subject of the next investigation which we carried out, this time with the mobile testing plant. It occurred to me at the time of writing these notes that there may have been a reason for choosing this one out of the four, and I turned up the report of the tests to see what conclusions were drawn. In view of the amount of effort put in, the results seemed hardly worthwhile. The author starts off by referring to the considerable variation in the handling of the engines, demonstrated by appreciable differences in the work done at the drawbar from day to day. The impression is that he is making his excuses before he gets to the nub of the matter!

A quick check shows that the train weights varied within the range 305 to 317 tons over the whole period, so there was no marked difference in what the engines were being asked to do. A further point was then made that the calorific value of the coal used for the Stephenson engine was 13,000 British thermal units per pound compared to 13,500 for the other three locomotives. We are then told that there were no marked differences in coal and water consumptions, this being followed by 'with regard to power development, the Caprotti engine was stronger in the gear, at earlier cut-offs, than the other engines'. The illustration for this statement is supposed to come from tables which give a whole lot of averaged figures for speed, drawbar horsepower, boiler and steam chest pressure, cut off and steam chest temperature for half a dozen selected stretches of the route. The variations in all the figures are such that I certainly would not like to say that any one of the four engines displayed any marked improvement in power output over its fellows without a lot of calculation to try to find common ground, so it seems to me that the above statement was almost more of a 'seat-of-the-pants' feeling than something that could be drawn from the figures. Reference is then made to the fact that the Caprotti engine showed about 50°F higher superheat than the other engines, 'probably accounted for by the 3⅝ in. blast pipe caps compared to the 3¾ in. on the other twin blast pipe fitted locomotives'. A final note pointed out that the Caprotti engine had 6 in. steam pipes in the smoke-box compared to 5 in. pipes on the other ones, but did not draw any conclusions as to what effect this might have.

With hindsight, one is left to feel that the procedure left a lot to be desired, and that there were so many variables involved that they prevented a useful conclusion, i.e. that a particular arrangement of engine was superior, being reached. I think that this is borne out by developments which came later, not only with the mobile test plant which gave the facility to run at a series of chosen speeds, and so plot a graph with points determined by the sub-test results, but also from the work carried out by Mr S.O. Ell at Swindon, which resulted in a testing technique which was adopted at Derby as well.

However I want to try to maintain a reasonable chronological sequence, so we must go back to No. 44764, and assume that this one was chosen because it

'Jubilee' class 4-6-0 No. 45578 *United Provinces* at Rugby shed on 27th February, 1950 with No. 3 Dynamometer Car and Mobile Test Units (MTUs) (one inside the shed). Note the frame carrying anemometer and wind direction indicator.
Author

was typical of the majority of the class '5' locomotives. Our test route was Derby to Willesden and back, via Leicester, Market Harborough, Northampton, Roade and so down the West Coast main line to Willesden. At that point, we serviced the train at Mitre Bridge which was the depot for the electric trains which ran to Euston, Broad Street, Richmond and Kew. As these were third rail, we had to watch where we put our feet. As I recall, we had no problems apart from one day when the fire hose with which we were filling the tender tank burst and shot a cascade of water all over a big light bulb which promptly exploded with a loud bang and a huge flash, and extinguished all the lights in half of the shed.

At this stage, the mobile test plant was still not fully operational, with items like the Farnborough indicator yet to be commissioned, the gas analysis panel had been installed and the weighing grate was still at the development stage, the first grate being designed for installation in No. 10897, the ex-L&Y 2-4-2T which was always known as 'Jane'.

All this work was proceeding under the direction of Dr H.I. Andrews of the Engineering Research Department, which was housed next door to the drawing office, and tended to be viewed by staff in the Chief Mechanical Engineer's Department as being full of airey-fairey, head-in-the-clouds scientists who would not know a regulator from a drain cock. Certainly some of them did not have a railway background, and there were one or two who did not appreciate the finer points of railway operation, but I came to know many of them over the years and came to appreciate the thoughts and ideas which resulted in developments like the mobile test plant.

The tests with No. 44764 lasted for three days, and were to some extent exploratory and gave us the opportunity to see how we could cope with a reasonably long out-and-home run. The round trip was 254 miles and as we ran on three consecutive days, by the time we had finished, we had had enough! There was virtually no break at the London end, as we had to reload the tender with bags of coal from the van, and on arrival back at Derby we had to load the tender *and* the van ready for the next day on the first two evenings. There was one blessing though, because we were using the corridor tender at least it was possible to leave the engine and go back to the dynamometer car while on the move and this fact gave me more opportunity to be in the cab, as the regular footplate observer asked for relief and I was sent to take his place for several spells.

It was on one of these occasions that I had quite a fright! In those days, I was not so able to 'read the road' as I was later, and this particular incident occurred as we were approaching Tring, running south. I had just done a 'round' of readings over the telephone reporting boiler and steam chest pressures, water level and the like and was standing behind the driver, looking ahead through his window. We were on a four track section, with the down fast on our right and the up and down slow to the left. I could see a freight train on the down slow in the distance, and when we were about a quarter of a mile away, it turned across in front of us. My immediate reaction was 'Good Heavens, we shall hit him!' but of course we didn't as we were crossing to the up slow at the same junction. I had not noticed the signals which told the driver what was going to happen and I can still recall that moment of panic quite clearly all these

Ex-Lancashire & Yorkshire 2-4-2T No. 10897 outside Derby No. 4 shed. Nicknamed 'Jane', this locomotive was used with the mobile test plant for many years after withdrawal from traffic in 1945. It retained its LMS logo and number when cut up in 1956. *Author*

Another view of 'Jane'. She is seen here at Rugby on 3rd March, 1950 setting off with No. 3 Dynamometer Car and three MTUs on a return trip to Peterborough. *Author*

years later and picture the grimy class '8' going across our buffers! After this series of tests, there was a quiet period when we did not seem to have a lot of outside work, and a considerable time was spent in the office. Vic Roberts decided that the opportunity should be taken to clear out a 'glory-hole' which was a partitioned-off corner in the corridor in which the section had squirrelled away all sorts of items for many years. Basil and I were each given a dust-coat - a boiler suit would have been much more protective - and left to get on with it. I can't recall many of the 'treasures' that were turned out, although I have no doubt that in the present climate for memorabilia, much that went for scrap would have been sought after today.

One item that I did manage to preserve was a General Arrangement of the GWR Pacific *The Great Bear* drawn to 1½ in. to the foot, and the associated valve gear arrangement which I think was drawn quarter full size. They were rolled up and yellow with age, but although tatty at the edges, nevertheless they were very interesting, especially as I had already begun to develop a high regard for Swindon and 'God's Wonderful Railway'.

In the course of my apprenticeship and afterwards, I became a sort of 'number-snatcher', and would travel to various places to watch trains go by. One of my favourites was Snow Hill station in Birmingham - quite easily accessible from Derby in little over an hour - and having arrived in that city at New Street, which was a filthy smoke-filled cavern of a place with a taxi-rank down the middle, a few minutes walk brought one to the spacious, clean platforms served by sparkling green engines and chocolate and cream coaches. And to hear a 'Castle' blast off with a Wolverhampton express with that distinctive clear-cut bark so characteristic of many of the Swindon designs, or to see a 'King' with 14 or 15 coaches coasting into the up side bound for Paddington was always a pleasure. I have no doubt that there were dirty panniers, 'Halls' and so on, but it was a superb station - alas, long gone.

Back to those *Great Bear* drawings, one of the most intriguing things about them was that they carried the stamp of the locomotive drawing office, Horwich, with a date in 1907 on them! Did the Lancashire & Yorkshire have aspirations to produce a Pacific? A 'Dreadnought' with a longer boiler, wide firebox perhaps, and that extra pair of wheels under the cab? Or perhaps they were going to stretch one of the seven foot Atlantics and put an extra set of cylinders on the front? What fun one could have with a sketch pad or drawing board scheming out such a 'might-have-been'. No-one I spoke to in the drawing office could cast any light on the reason for the drawings having been sent from Wiltshire to Lancashire 40-odd years before, but there must have been some ideas at Horwich . . . I wonder what they were?

Turning out took about a fortnight all told and though much was thrown out, a lot of items seemed to be taken by various draughtsmen for sentimental reasons because it reminded them of work done in the past. No doubt they were tucked away again in cupboards and drawers, maybe destined not to see the light of day again for many years.

In due course, the quiet period came to an end, and outside activity started up again. In February, at night, of course! It has to be more than coincidence that over many years of involvement in testing work it always seems that the majority falls in winter! Probably in fact, it is simply that one remembers the rigours involved, and tends to forget the times when the sun was shining (unless you were working in a warm firebox, so hot that it was cold to come out into temperatures in the high sixties, but that is a story to come much later). Anyway, February 1950 saw us involved in what were known as the Ideal Stocks trials, the purpose being to standardise the working arrangements for fast freight traffic throughout the Regions. Each former company had had its own ideas about working of freight traffic, ranging from the fully-fitted (i.e. vacuum brakes on all vehicles) Green Arrow traffic on the LNER for which the well known 2-6-2 locomotives were designed, and on which packets were distinctively marked with a green arrow symbol, through the part-fitted trains where a number of wagons behind the locomotive were fitted, with the rest not so equipped, down to the coal and mineral trains where the only brakes were those on the locomotive and the brake van.

We were involved in fully fitted class 'C' trains running between Somers Town Goods (next door to St Pancras) and Nottingham, and then the following week London to Ancoats, Manchester, as I said, these were overnight services, leaving an hour or two before midnight, and the purpose of the trials was to study the braking of the trains. This meant that we had to know precisely where we were, and to this end I was equipped with a car-type fog lamp run off the coach batteries and positioned at an open window to keep track of mileposts so that the driver could be told via the intercom system when to apply the brake. We made several tests in the course of each journey with the braking distance being measured in the test cars attached to the train. I was muffled up against the cold with numerous sweaters, overalls, great-coat, balaclava helmet, flying goggles, pilot's gloves and other impedimenta from the Army stores, and I was still perished! But it was fun, for all that. More than one courting couple, thinking themselves safely invisible at the end of a dark station platform, were rudely interrupted in their activities by my stabbing searchlight as we went tearing past.

I recall vividly, too, an incident at Kettering where we were detaching some wagons with hot boxes, how I was called on to try and sort out the stove in dynamometer car which had gone out. I cleared out the charred sticks and cold cinders, built up a new fire with several firelighters at the bottom, lit the fire and when it seemed well alight, I shut the door and busied myself elsewhere for a short time. I then went back to put the kettle on the stove, confident that it would be burning merrily. Opening the door of the little compartment, I was met by a thick acrid cloud of vile smoke which rapidly spread up the corridor, bringing Ernest down to see what was happening. I can't remember his exact words but they were not polite. The firelighters were made of shavings and a naptha-based substance and this was clinging in myriads of tiny flakes all over the stokehold walls. I diagnosed a blocked flue, so thought that it would be (a) expedient to try to clear it and (b) a good idea to make myself scarce until the smoke cleared!

Anyway, I climbed up on the coach roof with a sweeping brush, the handle of which I applied vigorously down the chimney. Suddenly, there was a 'woof' and smoke started to pour in thick clouds out of said chimney. Satisfied that the blockage had been disturbed, I climbed down, and by the time I reached the stove, it was roaring away a treat. Once we got on the move again, the induced draught made the back of the stove and the bottom of the stove-pipe glow red, something I had never seen before. Ernest had the decency to say I had made a good job, although he still thought I was a silly *** for using so many firelighters!

These were lodging jobs again, staying at Kentish Town which we knew well enough, and at Longsight in Manchester, which was fresh, and again was typical of the North Western barracks; reasonably clean and with a good canteen, but noisy as it was close to the running lines.

It is funny how little things stick in your mind like the time we arrived at Toton on one of the Ancoats trips. I had just been up to the engine to take a cup of tea to the footplate observer while the train crews were changed and was walking back to the coach when I found myself between two policemen who wanted to know where I was going! It turned out that trains such as we were running often carried commodities such as whisky, and railway police were on hand at booked stopping places to ensure no-one raided the train while it was stationary. We had not seen anyone at Kettering as the hot-boxes were out-of-course and we were not booked there.

Immediately we finished these runs, we were off to Rugby in March for work with the new No. 3 Dynamometer Car and the mobile testing units. My log shows that we ran between Rugby and Peterborough and Rugby to Leicester using class '5' engines although on one day, the L&Y 2-4-2T No. 10897 took us across to Peterborough. I well remember one of the Leicester trips where the 'Black Five' up front was slogging away while the MTUs kept the speed to a steady five miles per hour. We had the superintendent of the Rugby Testing Station on the train with us, and were listening intently to the exhaust beats, so clear cut that it was possible to detect that one of the four was just slightly more powerful than the other three, something that in normal service would never have been detectable. Mr Carling said that it was probably something that his chaps could never find, as they found that at low speeds and long cut-offs there was a strong tendency for the locomotive to slip. He put it down to the high polish that the rollers took on without the atmospheric conditions to promote rusting and hence a slight roughening of the surface, but more so to the fact that in the testing station the rails were about 18 feet long instead of several miles, being the circumference of the roller and quickly became contaminated with thrown oil which 'on the road' was spread over the much longer distance and was also removed periodically by rain. So he could never do as we were doing, developing a fair power at very low speed, and hence could not study exhaust beats as we were able to do.

Having satisfied ourselves that the mobile testing plant was functioning as it should, we had a final 'shake-down' day from Rugby to Willesden and back with 'Merchant Navy' No. 35005 *Canadian Pacific* an engine which I am pleased to see is presently undergoing restoration at Carnforth. In 1950, however, it had been fitted with a Berkeley mechanical stoker and was to be the subject of an extensive period of tests on the Southern Region. The run from Rugby up to Mitre Bridge was to make sure that the various 'blobs and gadgets' such as the

Ex-Lancashire & Yorkshire Railway 2-4-2T No. 10897 'Jane' at Peterborough with a mobile test plant run from Rugby on 3rd March, 1950. *Author*

The interior of No. 3 Dynamometer Car showing the recording table with integrator balls. The bank of pens are out of shot bottom right. *Author*

gas sampling for analysis, thermocouples in various places and that sort of thing were all working, before we left the Rugby 'base' for foreign parts. Obviously, the blue air-smoothed casing of the 'Navy' was a novelty and we attracted a lot of attention on this run, although I don't recall anything spectacular being attempted.

We did one or two 'shock-load' tests to check the control system on the mobile test units, simply by putting the steam reverser into full gear for half a minute or so. Incidentally, in the last chapter I said that similar tests were carried out in the initial commissioning of the mobile plant, and the tests were all carried out within the same series, the 'Merchant Navy' being our power on 8th March, while the shock-test run was carried out two days later, and was in fact the last run we made before the trials started on the Southern Region. We did one or two shock loads with *Canadian Pacific*, but it was necessary to be circumspect, to avoid pulling the fire to pieces. This was of less importance when we had the pilot Compound, so long as there was enough fire left to rebuild. And, of course, with the 4-6-0 engine* with its narrow firebox, the risk to the fire was less because of its thickness compared with the thinner fire in the wide box of the Pacific.

So it was that on 16th March we left Rugby, again behind *Canadian Pacific*. This time our destination was Stewarts Lane, where we were based for two months while we performed a most exhaustive series of tests on the 'Merchant Navy' running between Stewarts Lane and Salisbury. It was necessary to turn the train on a triangle, or at least the engine and dynamometer car, and such a facility existed at Salisbury, after which we went on to the shed for fire cleaning and water, etc., before setting off back to London. The tests did not occupy the whole of the two month period, and there were some gaps in the progamme.

One of the most vivid memories of these tests had nothing to do with railways in the true sense of the word, although rail-borne vehicles were involved. The Southern Region people had fixed up our accommodation in a large hotel on the south side of Clapham Common. Basil and I found that by the time we had paid the bill, we had precious little left out of the fixed expenses we were allowed, and pointed this out to Vic Roberts. The upshot was that we were given different rooms, which fronted onto the Common, and hence the line along which the all-night trams rattled and clanked every five or ten minutes throughout the night! So to save ourselves five shillings a night, we had to put up with the racket. Even then, we needed a bit of overtime every day to break even! Vic and Ernest, being on a higher expense rate, slept at the back, of course. I think that Charlie Sharpe, who was the footplate observer at the time, came to the front with us.

I found Stewarts Lane fascinating, both from the wealth of locomotive designs that I had not come across before, and the opportunity to observe these at close quarters. I remember being quite surprised to find a huge pile of Morse chains stacked against a wall, which one of the fitters explained came from 'Merchant Navy' and 'West Country' engines, and which it seemed had a tendency to stretch sufficiently to affect the valve events significantly. I was also able to go into the next door Longhedge works on several occasions for a look around.

* The runs referred to on page 35 included use of 'Jubilee' class No. 45578, both on its own, and with a pilot, the shock load being caused by setting it into full forward gear, and then opening the regulator fully.

'Merchant Navy' class 4-6-2 No. 35005 *Canadian Pacific* at Mitre Bridge Sidings, Willesden with No. 3 Dynamometer Car and two mobile test units during tests between Rugby and Willesden on 8th March, 1950. *Author*

Ex-LSWR Drummond 'T9' class 4-4-0 No. 30715 on Salisbury shed on 25th April, 1950. *Author*

The trials themselves were quite eventful; one day, for example, the tender had been filled with coal slack and fines, with nothing much bigger than a two-shilling piece (10 pence today). The mechanical stoker was quite able to deal with this, although the fireman was hard put to keep a reasonable depth of fire. The fuel tended to be drawn straight off the trays from which steam jets would have blown it on to the fire if it had been of normal size, straight through the tubes and out of the chimney. We were consuming - I can't say burning! - 140 to 150 lb. of coal per mile and our progress across the countryside was marked by the thick black pall of smoke which trailed behind us, which was reminiscent of the sort of thing one associated with American photographs of steam locomotives. Certainly it was not typical of British steam trains - heaven help any housewives who happened to choose that day to do the weekly wash.

Another incident that comes to mind involved Dr Andrews. On return to London, we had to turn the train again ready for the next day's run, and this involved running over the London Transport line from Wimbledon to Kensington Olympia, where a locomotive would be waiting to haul us backwards towards Clapham Junction, to enable us to be right way round when we stabled at the Lane. On this particular occasion, Ivan decided that this was an ideal opportunity to carry out a low speed test; after all, he was off the main line. So he twiddled the controls on his desk, to cause No. 35005 to start to bark asthmatically through the wide chimney as speed was pulled back to five miles per hour. This stately progress came to an abrupt halt when we came to a station when the locomotive inspector appeared, and pointed out that we were on an electrified line over which tube trains ran on about three minute headways! Ivan looked over his glasses at him, agreed that he would terminate his test, and we could proceed!

Off we went, but of course by then the damage had been done! It was late afternoon, probably about 5.30 pm, so he could not have timed it better to cause the maximum disruption. A little further on, at Kensington, there was a welcoming (?) committee and Dr Andrews was summoned to 55 Broadway the following morning to explain what he was up to! I found it most entertaining - he had done the same trick almost 12 months earlier when we moved the mobile test plant from Longsight to Cornbrook Sidings in the course of the Locomotive Engineers Summer Meeting, when he decided that it was an ideal opportunity for a walking pace test on the Manchester South Junction & Altrincham line, again a line with an intensive electric service. The results had been virtually identical with a red-faced inspector exploding into the coach after a sudden stop, breathing fire and brimstone and using language with a very ripe turn of phrase! Obviously, Ivan had forgotten. Needless to say, for the rest of the time with *Canadian Pacific*, he made sure that he had completed his day's programme before we reached Wimbledon!

'Royal Scot' class 4-6-0 No. 46155 *The Lancer* on the turntable at Camden on 4th September, 1950. It was being used for steam chest temperature tests on service trains between Euston and Carlisle and it was my lot to cover the Euston-Crewe and Crewe-Euston legs of the week-long tests. *Author*

No. 46155 *The Lancer* at rest at Camden shed during steam chest temperature tests on 4th September, 1950. *Author*

Chapter Six

Testing the first 'Britannia'

The work of the Locomotive Testing Section was very much a team effort, both at the time of execution of the tests and the subsequent analysis of the dynamometer charts, and observers' notes, followed by the preparation of graphs and writing of the report, although the last stage was really in the hands of Ernest Sharp and Vic Roberts. So it came as a bit of a surprise one day soon after the tests with *Canadian Pacific* finished, when Vic came to my drawing board and said he had a job for me, which I was to share with a fellow called Cliff, who had recently come to the section after serving his time at Horwich.

Measurement of steam temperature was always carried out by mercury bulb pyrometers, which had a long length of capillary tubing between the bulb, which was installed in the steam chest by means of an adaptor, and the dial housing, which we bolted to the cab roof, usually behind the driver's seat. There had been a query about the immersion depth of the bulb, and whether this could have any appreciable effect on the indicated temperature. So that this could be checked, a 'Royal Scot' engine going through Crewe works was going to have one of the outside steam chests drilled and tapped for two adaptors, close to one another. Vic told me to get on right away and draw up three adaptors to give three lengths of bulb exposure, and then to have these adaptors made in the locomotive works toolroom.

So it was that on 3rd September, 1950, I set off for Crewe with three adaptors. The pyrometers were already at Crewe North shed having been calibrated by the Area Chemists laboratory. At the shed, I found that the 'guinea-pig' was No. 46155 *The Lancer* and one of the shed fitters and I set to and fitted the pyrometers, using two of the adaptors. I went off to Gresty Road lodge for a few hours' sleep, then a meal in the canteen just by the horse dock, and finally to the North shed to meet the train crew who were going to work a train up to Euston. As I recall, it was about three o'clock in the morning when we left Crewe and after a few miles, long before we reached Stafford, I wondered what I was riding on! Lively was hardly the appropriate adjective, diabolical was probably nearer the mark. I had to keep using a torch to read the pyrometers, noting at the same time, cut-off and regulator, and it was a work of art to stand up, hold a pencil and notebook, a torch and have a hand free to hang on. It was a job for that Hindu god who has six arms! Fortunately the driver and fireman were very helpful and we found that with the firedoor slightly open, the torch could be dispensed with, except to read the cut-off. By driving on the regulator, that was not altered quite as much as might normally have been the case.

The driver told me that *The Lancer* had been back into the works for re-weighing three times since being out-shopped and in his opinion 'it's still a pig'. It did not deter him unduly and we romped along through the darkness. rolling and banging as if the engine was long overdue a general repair, instead of being fresh out of works. I can remember our progress through Harrow as it was coming light, I was sitting (?) on the fireman's seat with my ribs being battered by the cabside, and thinking of all the Londoners fast asleep behind the curtained windows flashing past, and not envying them one little bit.

In due time we rolled to a stop in Euston, and our bleary-eyed passengers walked by with hardly a glance, our train was hauled away, and then we proceeded tender-first up the bank to Camden. A set of shedmen took over the engine to see to coaling, fire-cleaning, and filling the tank, after which I was able to organise the swapping over of the pyrometer bulbs so that the one with the deepest immersion in the steam became the shallowest and vice versa. When that chore was completed, I thanked the foreman for the assistance and checked when the train crew were due to book on for our return to Crewe. Then I went off to find some breakfast, and bed in the Camden barracks.

After a good sleep I was up again in the late afternoon, went off 'up West' for a meal, most likely in Joe Lyons Corner House near Leicester Square, which had become a favourite haunt of ours, and then back to Camden for about nine o'clock, ready to meet up with the train crew again, and bring *The Lancer* down to Euston. We left there just before 11 pm and reached a Crewe soon after one in the morning. The train was continuing to Carlisle, and Cliff was on the platform to relieve me. I handed over the vital third adaptor which he was to have fitted at Upperby depot, watched as he climbed aboard, and waited until the train drew out and disappeared into the darkness.

As I walked along Gresty Road, I was wondering how Cliff was enjoying his 'baptism of fire'. He had never been on the footplate before and there he was, pitched into it in the middle of the night, on a locomotive which had refused to be balanced correctly on its springs and rode like a bucking bronco. At least my experience of footplate work was already well into a four figure mileage, so I knew a bit about it. I think that No. 46155 was about the liveliest engine I had so far come across, but there were others to come in the future which would eclipse its antics in no small measure.

I now had nearly 24 hours before I relieved Cliff on the up run the next morning. I slept until lunchtime and in the afternoon I went to Chester to look round the loco sheds there. Back in Crewe in the evening, there was time to go to the theatre which was usually a variety show of some sort, followed by a meal in the canteen, and to the station to meet the train in from Carlisle. Cliff had set up the third pyrometer comparison, and I had the last leg up to Euston to complete the tests. When the train came in, Cliff clambered down on to platform. 'Good trip?' I enquired. 'Bloody awful' was his reply. 'Why Cliff, I should have thought you would have enjoyed yourself. It's a good road from here to Carlisle', I said innocently. Cliff made some very disparaging remarks about the engine, and I just had time to assure him that I was thoroughly enjoying my trips. when the guard was whistling and I had to scramble aboard. This time I knew what I was in for and I thoroughly enjoyed the run. There is something different about a trip in the dark, with the glare of the fire reflected back into the cab from the exhaust steam streaming over the cab roof, and the inky blackness outside, the flickering green lights of the signals telling Line Clear Ahead, and every now and then, the splash through the pools of light at a station.

After the engine was disposed of at Camden, I had to have the pyrometers removed, coiled up and put into their boxes for return to Derby, together with the adaptors. The tapped holes were plugged securely and I took my leave of the foreman and made my way to St Pancras and so home, having had an enjoyable week working virtually on my own.

Back at Derby, we had a series of trips to Chinley with the No. 3 Dynamometer Car, usually with a Derby Compound 4-4-0. This involved turning both car and locomotive on the turntable in Chinley yard before the return run. As I recall, these runs were to sort out some minor problems with the recording equipment, and did not involve any real measurements on the locomotive.

A few weeks later, we started on a further series of tests with No. 44764 between Willesden and Stafford. The locomotive was pretty well fully instrumented, although I don't remember if the weighing grate was fitted. We ran from Derby to Willesden on 18th November and started the Stafford runs three days later. These tests renewed acquaintance with Dan Drury and, as at Holyhead 18 months earlier, we had the great pleasure of more of Dan's reminiscences as we sat around a roaring fire in the Willesden Lodge in the evenings.

No. 44764 once again had the corridor tender in tow, and Basil and I took turns as winch driver when coaling up. One feature which was a constant source of trouble during these runs was the water meter on the tender. This was positioned just in front of the rear buffer beam, and was basically very simple, being a hollow oval member with its major diameter a close fit in the circular chamber, while its minor diameter was snug about a large central pivot. The oval member had a wall thickness of about half an inch, and was about five inches wide, being a close fit in the depth of the shallow cylinder formed in the meter casing. In operation, each revolution of the meter delivered two gulps of water, the shape of a half moon, and five inches wide. I hope that description enables you to visualise the device. In practice, we found that it only needed a tiny bit of scale or grit to stop the rotor, which immediately caused the injector to knock off, as the water supply ceased. It became a matter of routine at Stafford that whoever was not winch driver, was water-meter stripper! Previously, one of us had been able to get a bite in the canteen. Towards the end of the tests, I got proficient enough to clean out the meter and close it up again in under half an hour and managed about 10 minutes for lunch as well. It was all right if you were over a pit, although the winch exhaust came rather close to the right ear, but without a pit it was a very awkward job. By observation, the meter usually packed in after we picked up water on the troughs and we reckoned that the turbulence caused rust particles to be stirred up. Someone was posted by the bypass valve when water pick-up was due, after a time, although what was really needed was a thorough cleaning of the tank!

Interspersed with the runs to Stafford were some on Sundays to Oxford, using an unusual route via Bletchley, Verney Junction, Bicester and into the LNW side at Oxford. For some reason, I can't recall much of what happened at Oxford - there is a vague recollection of a shed full of Great Western engines, but I can remember the superb roast pork, complete with apple sauce which was the dish-of-the-day in the canteen each Sunday we were there! I don't recall having to coal the tender either, but as Oxford is only 60-odd miles from London, whereas Stafford is 133, out and back on a load would be feasible.

Ex-LMS 'Black Five' No. 44764 at Stafford prior to a test run with mobile test plant back to Willesden in December 1950. *Author*

This series of tests covered a total of four weeks and finished in the middle of December. We must have collected a vast amount of data about class '5' engines, or at least about this example of the design! The report that was subsequently written was quite a thick one, if I remember rightly with masses of graphs included.

And so a New Year dawned, 1951, and with it the knowledge that the first of the BR Standard engines was soon to be unveiled. On 11th January, we took No. 1 Dynamometer Car across to Crewe, and into the North shed. The foreman told Vic that the engine was out on trials and would be back in about half an hour, so we went across to the Coffee Tavern on platform 3. This was a cosy little place with benches and tables covered with linoleum used by station staff, where you could get a drink, sandwiches, cakes too which were often home made. So after quarter of an hour or so, we came out and on to the footbridge which used to cross the north end of Crewe station. As we stood looking north, waiting for our first glimpse of this new locomotive, a chime whistle sounded, and there behind us on the through line next to No. 2 platform stood the black, gleaming No. 70000. So this was the Standard locomotive. As we watched, it eased away tender first under the bridge and across the North Junction on to the Chester line, obviously going on to the shed, to where we now returned with keen anticipation of a closer look, as we prepared for the run to Carlisle which was to take place on the following day. I do not need to detail what we found in our close up inspection, everyone knows the lines of a 'Britannia' although of course, at this stage, the engine was as yet unnamed, just the holes for the plates ready drilled in the smoke deflectors.

The test programme covered two days, 12th and 13th January, 1951. No. 70000 was to work Crewe to Carlisle on the first day, returning to Crewe the following day, the trains to be worked being normal services, the 12.50 pm down and the 11.52 up. These were non-stop between the two towns, although on the second day, a special stop had been provided at Preston, to enable senior railway staff who were riding on the locomotive to change places. The addition of the dynamometer car at the front of the train took the load to approximately 440 tons behind the tender, which was some 20 tons above the limited load for a class '7' locomotive when running to the timings for the two trains to be worked. Incidentally, to avoid any confusion, the power classification '7' under BR was equivalent to the LMS '6P', so No. 70000 was being compared to a 'Royal Scot' rather than a 'Princess Coronation', the latter being '7P' under LMS classification, but becoming '8' under BR and of course these Pacifics had a higher limited load than did a 'Scot'.

We spent the afternoon preparing No. 70000 on Crewe North shed, having coupled up to the No. 1 Dynamometer Car. This was what I would call a 'simple' test, basically measuring overall coal and water consumption, speed, drawbar pull and drawbar horsepower from the dynamometer chart and using mercury bulb thermometers for inlet and exhaust steam in one steamchest and at two points in the smokebox, close to the centre of the small tube bank and the centre of the large tubes, some six to nine inches away from the tube-plate. This meant that the footplate observer was a busy fellow, noting some nine different items, boiler and steam chest pressure, regulator opening, cut-off, water level and the four

My first sight of BR Standard 4-6-2 No. 70000 from the footbridge across the north end of Crewe station on 11th January, 1951. She moves off from No. 2 through road to go to Crewe North shed; the locomotive was painted plain black and un-named at this time. *(Both) Author*

temperatures noted above. In addition, he also jotted down passing times at the timing points along the route. In time to come, this became my duty and I can say that it can be no mean feat to scribble down all this data, whilst keeping one's balance, peering at the reverser over the driver's shoulder and at the same time keeping out of the fireman's way and remembering that the notes had to be legible later on. It really became difficult in the dark, when a torch was often needed to check on the readings and transfer them to the book. Of course, the engine crew and locomotive inspector would help tremendously, the driver often telling you when he adjusted his cut-off and regulator opening, while inspector and fireman could also be relied on to call out water level and pressures when they saw that a series of readings was being noted. It all became part of the team effort.

In due time, we came off shed and backed down on to the 12.50 train. As one would expect with senior staff aboard, a punctual departure was ensured and we headed North away from Crewe. The engine crew were Polmadie (Glasgow) men working the home leg of a lodging turn and had not had any 'familiarisation' with the engine, although of course they were accompanied by an inspector who had been out and about with No. 70000 in the days when it was running-in. The run to Preston was beset with speed restrictions, both permanent and temporary, the latter being for track repairs and we ran through Preston four minutes behind schedule.

The most spectacular event in the 51 miles was at Moore water troughs, just north of Weaver Junction, where the fireman got the scoop well down and was unable to retract it, with the result that the filler cover flew open and a solid column of water shot up and descended on the roof of the dynamometer car. The fountain was plainly visible through the large windows at the front of the car and lasted for what seemed an age. Speed at the time was about 60 mph, and as Moore is only about 21 miles from Crewe, there would probably be less than a thousand gallons consumed at that point - the official report showed a consumption of 30½ gallons per mile overall - so it can only be assumed that the fireman operated the 'dip' over-enthusiastically and of course, having got it in deep at that speed, it was beyond human strength to lift it out and you just had to wait until the track lifted the tender at the end of the troughs and relieved the pressure. I know just how the fireman must have felt, as it happened to me more than once; it would have been doubly embarrassing for him with a new locomotive and senior people riding in the train.

Once past Preston, No. 70000 was able to show her paces. Speed was up to 60 mph by Brock and we continued at this pace or more right away through Lancaster and Carnforth, over a relatively easily graded line. However, from Carnforth, the climb to Shap Summit, some 32 miles away, begins with a short 'breather' between Grayrigg and Tebay as the line finds its way through the Lune Gorge, before the final four miles at 1 in 75 to pass the Summit itself. Speed fell off gradually as we climbed from Milnthorpe past Oxenholme, with a view over Kendal on our left and was down to just over 40 mph at Grayrigg. The Lune Valley enabled the train crew to build up speed again past Low Gill and Dillicar troughs so that we passed Tebay at 66 mph having gained four minutes on schedule from Carnforth. Our headlong progress continued past Scout Green, so beloved of railway photographers in steam days, and with a

BR Standard No. 70000 at Crewe North shed on 11th January, 1951 being prepared for a test run to Carlisle on the following day. *Author*

BR Standard No. 70000 standing on Carlisle Upperby shed on 12th January, 1951 at the end of a run from Crewe for senior railway staff. *Author*

minimum speed of 36 mph we passed Shap Summit having gained almost three minutes on the climb from Tebay. The report quotes an average drawbar horsepower of 1,548 and an average speed over the four mile climb of 44½ mph, the power developed being equivalent to a figure, corrected for the gradient, of 1,892 drawbar horsepower.

From Shap to Carlisle it is downhill all the way. In fact, in the cutting just south of the summit, there is a bridge which is still referred to as the Bridge of Sighs, obviously of relief on the part of the fireman as he realised that the hard work was over and he could stop shovelling, let his fire burn through, unless of course he was going through to Glasgow, but even then he could ease up for the next 30 miles at least. Speed soon increased on the down grade, to around 70 at Clifton and after checking to 55 through Penrith, a maximum of 78 was reached before braking and gliding to a stand in Citadel station, three minutes early. No. 70000 and the dynamometer car were uncoupled and proceeded to Upperby loco, where the coal remaining was weighed and the tender refilled ready for the run on the following day. The engine was then stabled in the relatively modern round-house at Upperby - I can recall standing in front of No. 70000 later that evening with Charlie Sharpe, who was the footplate observer, when Mr E.S. Cox came down the side of the engine and stood talking to us for some 20 minutes or so, discussing points of the design and construction. What foxes me is what we did with the dynamometer car, because we could not put locomotive and car on the turntable together, so either we must have uncoupled the car, or stabled on the far side of the turntable opposite to one of the access roads. Funny isn't it how some little details like this are clouded over by time?

As well as having a modern round-house, Upperby also boasted a modern hostel, with individual rooms, spring interior mattresses on the beds, recreation room and so forth. It stood on a hill directly above the depot and there was also a modern canteen block adjacent as well. Little did I know that this, my first visit, was going to be one of very many and the place would almost become a second home for a time. We spent the evening in the canteen and then sallied forth to sample the delights of Carlisle.

The following day dawned bright and dry and we busied ourselves with preparations for the return run to Crewe, although as our departure was not until 11.52 am, we were able to have a leisurely breakfast - a good job, because they were enormous! You started off with a big plate of porridge, presumably because of the proximity of Scotland although drivers from north of the border would never stay at Upperby - it seems it was built on ground where the English used to hang marauders from the other side of Hadrian's Wall! Bacon, eggs, sausage and tomato were standard fare with doorsteps of bread and huge mugs of tea.

With that fortification, we moved the locomotive out into the yard, topped up the water in the tender and set back down to the station. Quite a crowd had gathered to see us leave, the word must have spread rapidly the previous afternoon and evening. As would be expected, we left on the dot and the Upperby enginemen took to No. 70000 like a duck to water, succeeding in cutting almost seven minutes off the schedule to Shap Summit. The downhill stretch to Carnforth was run in a restrained manner, with speed up to about 77 maximum and two permanent way slacks at Grayrigg and Lancaster reduced our early running to just under four minutes by the time we stopped at Preston. This was not a scheduled stop and was for members of the senior staff to change places on the footplate, so we were soon on the move again, leaving Preston with nearly two minutes in hand. As on the previous day, the Preston to Crewe section was beset by permanent way work and we were in deficit by Euxton Junction. An effort was made to counteract the effects of the slacks and we passed Winsford half a minute to the good, only to see it disappear into a three minute late arrival due to a slack at Minshull Vernon and a signal check at Coppenhall Junction. However, everyone seemed highly satisfied with the proceedings of the two days and the results of the second day's test gave better coal and water figures than for the first day and the climb from Carlisle to Shap produced a long period of sustained power, although the outputs achieved on the down run were not repeated.

I must say that I was most impressed, even if I was still at an impressionable age! Here was a superb looking, simple locomotive with a lot of features designed to make it easy to maintain, which could handle trains over its load limit with ease. It seemed to me that it really was a winner and it took me back to the days when Harold Allwood, who had his board next but one ahead of me, would explain most patiently how he was setting about the boiler design and now here it was, transformed into three dimensional steel and how well it looked to me. It was years later that I suddenly spotted a feature of all the other Standard classes for that matter, which provided the link with Horwich, where Mr Cox had spent so much of his early railway career. At the time I was scheming out drawings for an L&Y railmotor of the type that used to work the Horwich 'Jerk' from Blackrod, in 7¼ in. gauge. I had completed the elevation of the engine unit and it happened that the drawing had other papers lying on top of it, such that only the top half of the chimney was visible. It was then that I realised that the Standard locomotive chimney was a direct descendant of the L&Y pattern. The chimney on a steam locomotive is a very distinctive feature and when copied for a Small Locomotive, it can make or mar the end result to a very marked degree, so that it is imperative that considerable care is taken to make a true-to-scale copy.

The BR Standard locomotives are not often ascribed to the CME in the same way that those of pre-Nationalisation or pre-Grouping companies were for that matter, where we talk of McIntosh, or Drummond, or Churchward, Stanier, Gresley, etc. Occasionally R.A. Riddles is mentioned, but more often than not, the engines are BR, not linked to a person, or a place - such as Swindon, or Crewe or St Rollox. But for me, ever since that day I recognised a chimney, BR Standard designs are linked in my mind with Horwich.

On reaching Crewe with No. 70000, we uncoupled and ran to Crewe North with the dynamometer car, carried out the coal weighing routine, prepared the car for its journey back to Derby, and then made that journey ourselves. Before we left Crewe, we knew that the subject of our tests was to be named 'Britannia' and that this would be the class name as well. It was a design with which we would be involved on numerous occasions subsequently, as you will see as my Privileged View of Steam enables me to share my experiences with you . . .

Chapter Seven

Locomotive Testing on the Settle & Carlisle

After the 'Britannia' tests, we started to prepare for a series of tests with an LNER 'B1' 4-6-0, using a new technique of constant steam rate testing based on a system developed at Swindon by Mr S.O. Ell. The blast pipe was used as a nozzle, and a mercury manometer was coupled to a tapping a short distance down from the blast pipe cap. The manometer was carried in the dynamometer car and connected to the locomotive by small bore tubing with rubber connections between engine and tender, and tender and car. Once the flow rate for the test had been chosen, and the mercury height corresponding had been worked out, the balance was maintained from a pre-charged air reservoir, pumped up at intervals by a tyre pump, and checked with a 'bubble jar' to prove that air was flowing, as shown by the steady stream of bubbles. A slave manometer was coupled into the line, and positioned at the driver's side where he could see it easily. This manometer had an adjustable pointer which was set, and, during the test, the driver maintained the mercury miniscus at that level by adjustment of the cut-off.

We had been discussing the development of the constant steam-rate system for some time and I recall one of our journeys back to Derby when Ernest Sharp was saying that we were going to be told to apply the system to our tests, and he commented that we would need to find a route which was predominantly rising for a good few miles. I suggested that the old Midland route between Leeds and Carlisle had a long climb in both directions, with of course a long downhill stretch to follow, the latter not being of any use for testing as you could not keep steam on to any extent downhill, unless the mobile test plant was used. The intention was that this method of testing would be covered by the old L&Y No. 1 Dynamometer Car. Ernest did not say much at the time but in due course my suggestion bore fruit, and our regular test route became Carlisle to Skipton and return, with the train being turned on the triangle at Shipley.

In March 1951 I paid a couple of visits to Rugby, to go to the Testing Station where No. 61353 was undergoing trials. My visits were to arrange for certain modifications to be made to engine and tender, notably a series of tubular 'arches' over the coal space, to which netting was attached, so that the two men who rode in the tender and emptied the bags of coal into a hopper on the shovelling plate, would be prevented from putting their heads 'out-of-gauge' and being injured by a bridge. Other items were to see that the wooden hopper unit fitted properly and was secure and also the injector overflow tanks, which caught any discharged water. These had to remain within the loading gauge and it became my job from the beginning to scheme out the largest tank possible, and arrange the indicator in the cab to show when it was full, and also a method of emptying.

My method was rather Heath Robinson, with a float about the size of a large fruit salad tin, but made of heavier gauge tinplate in the tinsmiths shop. The top

'B1' class No. 61353 at Rugby Test Plant moving between the test hall and the preparation shed at the end of a day's testing. *Author*

Ex-Furness Railway 0-6-0 No. 52494 at Moor Row engine shed on 28th April, 1951. *Author*

had a turned brass blind housing for a large rubber bung, the bung being bored for a long garden cane, this passing through a hole in the cab floor, so that its tip moved up and down in a slotted tube marked F (full) and E (empty). I calibrated each tank - they usually had a capacity of between six and eight gallons. When full, a length of chain or Bowden cable through another hole in the floor lifted a large brass plug, like an overgrown bath plug to empty the tank. The method worked well, the only minor problem being that the float, which was guided by a length of superheater flue, would sometimes tend to jam, but this was cured by soldering two rings of thick wire round the float near the top and bottom. After that, no more difficulties.

Towards the end of April, we set off with the dynamometer car, coupled on the back of one of the Derby to Crewe trains. On arrival at Crewe, the vehicle was uncoupled and shunted to meet up with the test locomotive which had run light from Rugby. On this particular day, I first made the acquaintance of Henry Powell, the locomotive inspector from Rugby. Henry was a Welshman, originating I think from somewhere near Swansea. He invariably accompanied the test engine through to Carlisle and I had many pleasant trips in his company. Sometimes he would stay overnight too, and we were treated to another fund of yarns equal to those of Dan Drury.

On arrival at Carlisle, we turned right from Upperby to Petteril Bridge Junction and so on to the Midland line and thence into Durran Hill. This ex-Midland shed, which was a Kingmoor outstation, became our base, and in the same way Upperby hostel became our 'home'. As they were about 10 minutes walk apart, it was quite a satisfactory arrangement. We had already found out a bit about Carlisle when we came with 'Britannia', but now that we were there for a week, we were able to explore further. Most of our needs were catered for by the hostel and the canteen, although we did find a cafe run by an Italian family in Botchergate which provided some variety - spaghetti instead of - or with - chips! Our other port-of-call became the Friars Tavern, mainly because Vic and Ernest, who were the experts in these matters, pronounced the State brew as awful, and the Friars was the only place where Bass was on draught! My palate was not so developed at that time, and I mostly drank cider!

According to my log, I went with the train to Skipton and back on Tuesday, Wednesday and Thursday, while on Friday I went to Whitehaven and Workington. Then on Saturday/Sunday I came back to Derby via Leeds. I can't remember the details now, but I think that these tests were a sort of 'shake-down' for us to find our feet with the new system, and that we only did three round trips. I was left behind to bring the dynamometer car back, which explains why I went to Workington - filling in time. In fact I think that was when I went to Moor Row shed and took some shots of an ex-Furness railway 0-6-0. That bit would not show in the log as it was a bus journey! Certainly the Saturday/Sunday journey home - I can recall many of those!

The car was conveyed in a parcels train which left Carlisle not long before midnight. Despite the fact that it was supposed to be all arranged beforehand, I don't think there was ever a trip when I did not have to explain somewhere along the line what was supposed to happen to the car. I hate to think what might have happened if it had not been accompanied. In fact, at the back of my

'B1' class 4-6-0 No. 61353 at Skipton North after having turned engine and dynamometer car at Shipley, ready for the return to Carlisle in April 1951.
Author

A view over the tender of 'B1' class 4-6-0 No. 61353 showing the coal men who emptied the 1 cwt sacks of coal into the hopper for firing and the net and its supports designed to keep their heads 'in gauge'. *Author*

Footplate crew, *left to right*, London Midland Region CME J.F. Harrison, inspector Sandy Willis, driver Frank Dowell and fireman Joe Armstrong with 'B1' No. 61353 at Skipton North Junction in April 1951. *Author*

BR Standard 'Britannia' class 4-6-2 No. 70009 *Alfred the Great* at Euston on 18th May, 1951 ready for a demonstration run for the technical press to Rugby and back. The No. 1 Dynamometer Car is behind the tender. *Author's Collection*

BR Standard 'Britannia' class 4-6-2 No. 70009 *Alfred the Great* on arrival at Rugby from Euston with a press run on 18th May, 1951. *Author*

mind lurks the feeling that on this my first trip, there was confusion at Citadel station on Friday night, resulting in the car not being positioned to be coupled to the train, and that was why it was Sunday before I got home. Happy days!

They were too, and quite a few of these journeys were enlivened by having enginemen for company to Hellifield or Skipton or even Leeds. The presence of the car was a god-send to these fellows, who were then able to 'hitch a lift' back home, this often meaning several hours difference to them. If often meant that I could not get my head down for a snooze, as we only had six seats in the riding compartment, so it soon became too full for me to stretch out.

The middle of May saw us heading south to London, again with the No. 1 Dynamometer Car, via Rugby to Euston and then to Camden. The occasion was a run for the benefit of the Press, particularly the technical people, to show off the paces of a 'Britannia'. The engine chosen was No. 70009 *Alfred the Great*, and on 18th May, we backed down into Euston with the car, to couple to our train. This was a special, with ample catering facilities, and we were to work it to Rugby at which point our passengers would be able to visit the Testing Station and see another member of the class, No. 70005 *John Milton* being put through its paces. I can't remember the precise timing, but I am fairly certain that lunch was served on the train after arrival at Rugby.

What I do remember, as if it was yesterday, was the trip to Northampton which was undertaken with *Alfred the Great* to turn. For some reason, Rugby only had a small turntable, incapable of dealing with a 'Britannia'. A colleague once described seeing the performance when they turned *Canadian Pacific*, it was necessary to position the rear tender wheels as close as possible to one end of the rails, and then jack up the bogie leading axle because the flanges fouled the track leading to the table!

Anyway, on 18th May, it was decided that No. 70009 and the car would go to Northampton to turn on the triangle. We set off at a cracking pace with the 'Britannia' going backwards and propelling the car. Soon we were doing over 60 mph and suddenly there was a tremendous bang and a crash, and a howling gale swept through the vehicle, filling the place with dust, sheets of paper and so forth. Basil and I, who had been left in charge, investigated and found that the corridor vestibule door was wide open, the air pressure having burst the catch out of the jamb! It took our combined strength to push the door to against the blast, and bolt it, with the two bolts top and bottom. We did not have much faith in their strength however, and used a couple of sweeping brushes, wedged under the handle and against the cupboards opposite to provide additional security. Our headlong flight continued on the return journey too, but our 'jury rig' stood up to the test. It turned out that the locomotive inspector had been invited to take lunch on the train and had left the train crew to their own devices, and they obviously wanted to see how *Alfred the Great* would go, even backwards!

We had had a good run down in the morning, and the press men had come through in groups to see what we were doing, and to have the testing techniques explained to them. Going back up in the afternoon, there were fewer visitors, presumably because they preferred to sit and chat after their lunch and drinks. However, one small group did form in the dynamometer car, namely

The interior of No. 1 Dynamometer Car during a demonstration run between Euston and Rugby on 18th May, 1951. The author is on the left, Vic Roberts in the foreground, Ernest Sharp behind the recording table and Cliff Belfield on the right.
Author's Collection

'Britannia' class 4-6-2 No. 70009 at Rugby after the hair-raising propelling run with Dynamometer Car No. 1 to Northampton and back on 18th May, 1951. *Author*

Messrs C.J. Allen, J.N. Maskelyne and O.S. Nock, and it was fascinating to watch their reactions while they were there. As it happened, they were treated to some fast running from Tring southwards, and they were almost jumping up and down with excitement as the speedometer needle crept round steadily to 90 mph. To me at the time, these men were well known people whose writings were widely published, and yet here they were, obviously highly enthusiastic and ready to chat to any of us, even we, the juniors! It made our day too!

On arrival at Euston, quite a few people stuck their beads into the car to say thank you, a gesture which was appreciated, and then after the train had been hauled away, the car was trundled out to Willesden and stabled. My notes tell me that once more I was left in charge and that it was three days later before an empty stock working took me via Rugby, Leicester and Nottingham, and then to Derby.

Two days later, I was back at Rugby, this time overseeing the fitting up of *John Milton* for road testing. A further trip one week later to see that everything I had asked for had been done, and then on the last day of May to Crewe to meet Henry, and on to Carlisle. He was full of enthusiasm for No. 70005, tempered with a footplateman's knack of spotting problems.

One which was coming to light was that if a driver used the handle on the reverser handlewheel, which had its spindle centre line horizontal, across the locomotive, and then driving through right-angle bevels and a universally-jointed shaft to the screw which was immediately behind the weighshaft, he would be lucky to avoid barking his knuckles, in some cases quite badly.

BR Standard 'Britannia' class 4-6-2 No. 70005 *John Milton* on the up loop line, Skipton North Junction for the northbound test run on 12th June, 1951. *Author*

'Britannia' class No. 70005 *John Milton* at Skipton engine shed ready for the northbound test run on 13th June, 1951. *Author*

Above: 'Britannia' class No. 70005 *John Milton* ready to leave Durran Hill up sidings on 15th June, 1951. Durran Hill (NE) signal box is partially hidden by the locomotive. *Author*

Left: The overflow tank fitted to the exhaust injector of No. 70005 *John Milton*. A float moved a garden cane through a hole in the cab floor to indicate when the tank was full; a cord lifted a brass 'bath plug' (a big one!) to empty. It was a bit 'Heath Robinson', but it gave a measure of water loss at the injector. *Author*

Drivers who had been so caught then altered the gear by pulling the rim of the wheel, which became a time consuming operation if reversal was called for. Some engines were worse than others because it was a pipe run and the clips thereon which caused the problem, if I recall correctly. Frank Dowell, who was our regular driver on the Skipton run, certainly made a nasty mess of his right hand with *John Milton,* and had a few choice words to say about the reverser! It was certainly much more difficult to work than the gear on a Stanier engine, which, once the stiff newness had gone, could be almost effortless in use.

We had only managed a couple of days of tests with *John Milton* when we broke the dynamometer car, or at least a part of it. On the second day, we were on our way back to Carlisle when the paper stopped moving across the recording table, and, simultaneously, a banging noise started underneath the vehicle. The train was quickly brought to a stand, and Vic and Ernest got down to investigate. They soon found that the shaft from the road wheel gearbox was resting on the track where a block forming the centre piece of a universal joint had split in two. Half of it was missing. That put paid to any further testing, the road wheel was raised and Basil and I were sent underneath to secure the broken shaft to the underframe. On arrival back in Carlisle, we were 'volunteered' to return to Derby on a train which left the Citadel a few minutes after midnight. The plan was that one of us would go into the locomotive works toolroom, while the other went home, and then in the afternoon we would change over, and when the new spider was ready, we would return to Carlisle. Vic said he would ring the works and arrange everything, but in the event I was in the toolroom before he got through, so that when he did, the job was already in hand.

Certainly, all the stops were pulled out and about 24 hours after setting off from Carlisle, we were on our way back, and were able to go straight to Durran Hill, repair the shaft, and go to the canteen for breakfast. We were already sitting down when Vic and Ernest came in.

'Hello boys', said Vic, 'back already. Where is the block?'

'Sorry Vic, it's not here', I said.

'Why have you come back then' says he, and seeing that his temper was rising fast, I admitted that it was in its right and proper place! He was like a dog with two tails, gulped his breakfast down and dashed off to check that he was satisfied with what we had done. He was, and we went out on test that day, so in all we only lost one and half runs. Unfortunately, it was somewhat spoilt when some officious clerk declared that we would not be paid for travelling from Carlisle to Derby and back again. We were annoyed, to put it mildly, and pointed out that if we had not done what we did, Vic would have lost three whole days at least. The point was conceded, and we got the money. It made up for the lack of sleep!

These tests occupied a full fortnight and we certainly gave that engine some work to do. As I mentioned earlier, we had a regular driver, Frank Dowell, in fact we had a regular footplate crew, Sandy Willis was the inspector, and Joe Armstrong was the fireman. On days when we were doing a high steaming rate, a second fireman came along, another Joe, although I can't remember his surname. This was because firing rates got too high to be sustained for a long test by one fireman, and it was helpful too if one was opening and closing the doors to keep the cold air ingress to a minimum. We also had regular men in the tender who volunteered for the work. It was hard, dirty work, surrounded by clouds of dust, wet and cold if the weather was inclement, and a steam engine tender is not noted for its exceptional riding qualities either!

About the actual testing, there is not much I can say. The run from Carlisle to Appleby through the Eden valley climbs steadily but not steeply and speeds well up into the 70s were not unusual. After Appleby, the hard collar work starts with a ruling gradient of 1 in 100 all the way up to Ais Gill summit. The line then undulates over the next 10 miles through Hawes Junction - now Garsdale - and Blea Moor tunnel to Ribblehead where it starts the plunge down past Horton and Settle to Hellifield. Up over a hump and then downhill again to Skipton North Junction, where we stabled our train, just taking the dynamometer car and van with the coal bags on to Shipley to turn. An arrangement with the refreshment room manageress, organised by Vic Roberts, resulted in us being served lunch there each day. Then we would rejoin the train, and organise the loading of the tender. At first, we went on to Skipton Loco, but one day we got stuck! I can't remember whether it was No. 61353 or 61351, which was next after No. 70005, but anyway, there we were, all ready to go. Frank opened the regulator, nothing happened. He pulled the gear right back and cracked the regulator again, finally opening it to more than half which should have had us chuffing smartly on our way. Same result, no movement. Check that the tender handbrake is off, it is, and try backgear again. Still no movement. Sandy and Joe get down, one each side, while Frank tries forwards yet again. The inspector and the fireman meet at the front of the engine, and then walk back down each side, Sandy then comes to the cab and calls up, 'The brake's on'. Frank indignantly denies that it is, and Sandy goes for another look. 'It is so', he says. Frank climbs down and agrees that the blocks are hard on the driving wheel.

By this time, we were all gathering round and then someone pointed out that the wheel was right over a joint. A Jinty is called up to give us a nudge, in fact a mighty heave is needed, but once we get the driving axle out of the hole it has dropped into, all is well again. However, an alternative site is sought to do our loading, and we start to use the Ilkley line arrival platform. This in fact makes things much easier, as the coal only has to be lifted from platform level, not off the ground.

Servicing completed, it is back to Skipton North to pick up the train again. Off we go, and start to climb straight away, up through Bell Busk, dropping down into Hellifield, through Long Preston to Settle Junction. Bearing to the right, the line starts to climb straight away up the Long Drag, 15 miles at 1 in 100 to Ribblehead viaduct. This is our test section going home, possibly extended through Blea Moor tunnel towards Dent. But once we pass Hawes Junction, which in those days still had its turntable with the famous fence of on-end sleepers round it, reputedly because on one occasion the wind took charge and kept an engine turning on the table for some hours, we have finished. We pass Ais Gill summit, and coast down Mallerstang towards Appleby and Carlisle.

As we lads had quite a bit to do when we finally got back to Durran Hill after the train had turned, we got into the habit of buying the makings of a meal in Skipton, and one of us would take his turn to act as cook using the coal-fired stove. Dinner was usually served somewhere beyond Appleby and there was no need to rush; even a three course spread left time for washing up before coaling time!

It was around this time that Basil left the railway and went to Rolls Royce. His place was taken by another ex-Derby works 'Priv', Pat Webb, who in fact started his apprenticeship on the same day as me, and was responsible for lighting the flame of enthusiasm in me, explaining how locomotives were allocated to depots, and did not just run about willy-nilly, but worked in diagrams. I also learned how to identify the home depot, by the cast plates on the smokebox door of an LMS engine, with the code of numbers and letter, or the cryptic letter code on the footplate valance of a GWR engine, or maybe the far easier LNER system with the depot name, occasionally abbreviated, on the front buffer beam. The Southern always remained a mystery! I think it is true to say that my enthusiasm is still there, for railways of all sorts, but for steam in particular.

It was on the next series of tests between Carlisle and Skipton, with the 'B1' No. 1351 that I took over the footplate work. One day, we had just left Carlisle when the train suddenly pulled up, I think it was Cotehill station. Anyway, Joe Armstrong burst in and said, 'Charles is poorly'. Charles Sharpe had 'cornered the market' and considered the footplate was his domain, and moreover, because it was such an arduous job, he had convinced Vic that it was too much to expect him to do anything else. So he was excused coaling and so on, and used to roll up half an hour or so before we were due off shed, usually when the tea was mashed! At the day's end, he used to disappear with equal alacrity! But back to Cotehill. Charles was helped into the coach looking very grey and groggy. Vic flung a boiler suit at me - I was looking after the master manometer, a dust-coat job - and said, 'Get up on the engine quickly' - which I did, changing into the boiler suit as we got on the move again. Charles recovered to be able to stay on the train, but his doctor advised that he should stay off the footplate which, although I was sorry to see a chum suffering ill health, suited me all the same. Oddly enough, I was never excused coaling duties, and was expected to be down to breakfast with the rest!

I think that one of the reasons that we had No. 61351 and its sister No. 61353 was because the Midland Region chief mechanical engineer was Mr J.F. Harrison, who had come from Doncaster. Certainly, on one trip from Skipton to Carlisle, I was asked to stand down so that Mr Harrison could take my place. There was considerable interest in the 'B1' which had the same 6 ft 2 in. coupled wheels as the Standard class '5', construction of which was just starting. Frank Dowell and Joe Armstrong were not impressed with the LNER engine, and Joe told me that he found it a very unforgiving engine to fire, liable to lose its pressure if you turned your back! Both he and Frank said give them a 'Black Five' every time, but then they were used to them and knew how to handle them.

No. 61351 occupied our time for a fortnight as had No. 70005. My notebook tells me that at the end of both series of tests, someone else brought the car back to Derby. At least my return trips are both shown via Crewe, and I don't think I ever came back with it on that route.

Other gems which I pick out from my book are that between *John Milton* and the 'B1' I had a holiday in Ireland. I have an entry 'Waterford-Dublin-Kingstown' which was when the magneto on my motorcycle packed in and we had to come home on the train. And then after the 'B1', in September there are entries Derby-Liverpool and Liverpool-Derby, with in between 'Douglas-Ramsey'. I can only assume I came back from Ramsey on the bus. Certainly one purpose of the trip was the Manx Grand Prix, which I think was rained off and gave me the opportunity to sample the delights of the Isle of Man Railway, now sadly but a shadow of its former self, but at least still steam worked.

The end of October and early November 1951 saw me once again at Rugby, this time readying No. 73008 for road tests. By the middle of the month we were plugging away with this engine, mentally comparing it with the Stanier 'Five'. Sandy Willis used to instruct Frank to try certain things. He had his own ideas about coasting, and he liked to run with the gear pulled up nearer to mid-gear than the indicated D (drift) position. When we tried this with No. 73008, we got a most pronounced whistle at the chimney top. Sandy tried everything, including cracking the regulator, but all to no avail. Drop the gear down to 'D' and the whistle became a whisper - you could detect it if you listened, but most folk would not notice. In the end Sandy gave up, told Frank to coast at 'D' and passed round his sweeties. This was a ritual on the footplate.

As soon as we passed Ribblehead going South or Ais Gill going North, Sandy would bring out his bag of sweets, usually mints or toffees and pass them round to us, first Frank, then Joe, then me. He never had a lot to say, but he was a very friendly man once you knew him. He never did say what a Caley man thought of running over the Midland. Frank had been on the South West but had run to Leeds for years. Joe, of course, had no allegiance to a pre-Grouping company, and was LMS through and through. He was one of those men who lived for his work, and was for ever striving to improve. He later became an inspector himself, but alas died some years ago. It is perhaps a measure of his enthusiasm for his life's work that he directed in his will that his ashes should be scattered at Ais Gill summit.

At the end of the two weeks, all three pronounced themselves well pleased with the Standard Five; it was almost brand new when we had it. Frank thought it was one of the most free-running engines he had ever driven, Joe, naturally, was impressed by the steaming of the boiler with which he never had a moment's problem, even at the highest rates we imposed on him and his colleague. Sandy simply said in his rich Scots brogue, 'Tis a guid strong ingin', which really said it all.

BR Standard class '5' 4-6-0 No. 73008 standing at Durran Hill siding ready for departure to Skipton in November 1951. *Author*

No. 73008 at Skipton North Junction ready for return to Carlisle on 17th November, 1951. *Author*

Chapter Eight

Some Unofficial 'Driving Turns'

The tests with the BR Standard class '5' No. 73008 took us to the end of November 1951, and my only activity in the remainder of the year outside the office was a run from Toton Sidings to Brent (Cricklewood) with a vacuum-fitted train of loaded mineral wagons. We had two LMS class '5' engines, No. 44667 piloting No. 45342, these being a class with which Toton men did not have a lot of experience. I was the footplate observer on the train engine and soon after we set off, I noticed that there was a lot of vibration under my feet, but I did not think much of it at the time. We took the route via Melton Mowbray and Manton from Syston, rejoining the main line at Glendon Junction, just north of Kettering. We had an uneventful run as I recall, and I can't remember if we ran any hot boxes - we were running up to 65 mph - all the wagons being loaded to capacity, and we were dragging 40 of them along behind us. We stopped at Wellingborough for water, although of course, we also picked up on the troughs, with the pilot taking first 'dip' and leaving the second half for us. This, however, usually meant that neither fireman was able to replenish his tank completely, hence the Wellingborough stop to top the tanks right up.

On arrival at Brent, we put the train away and took the engines across to Cricklewood Loco. As we walked down the path from the shed to catch a bus into London, my legs felt quite tired. I suppose the bus ride took about 20 minutes, and it was the first time I had sat down since leaving Toton. The bus stop was near Euston, and when I came to get up, my legs felt awful! We had to walk along Euston Road to St Pancras, and by the time we reached the station, it was quite painful to walk, and got worse with every step, so that by the time we were walking along the platform, each step was agony making me grit my teeth with pain. I had never before experienced anything like it, nor have I since in many thousands of miles on the footplate. It was muscular and I suspect that it might have been because we were double-headed and due to some extent to 'shuttling' between the two locomotives. Whatever it was, the long Sunday journey back to Derby gave me time to recover and the pain had gone when we got home.

A similar run with 70 loads, hauled by two 'Britannias', was made a fortnight later. My only involvement was to get up and ride out to Kegworth on my motorcycle on a grey, cold morning to try to get a photograph. As it was about half past seven in the morning, the result was awful, even after trying to intensify the negative. It was a superb sight, however, with clouds of exhaust, and the long train snaking away into the dim distance.

Mid-January 1952 found me down at the Rugby Testing Plant, and in the works adjacent to the shed, finalising the arrangements for fitting out No. 70005 *John Milton* ready for a full scale series of tests between Carlisle and Skipton which were going to last three weeks. So it was that on Friday 24th January we took the No. 1 Dynamometer car across to Crewe on the rear of a service train,

Ex-LMS 'Black Five' 4-6-0 locomotives Nos. 44667 and 45342 taking water at Wellingborough *en route* from Toton to Brent sidings with 50 loaded 16 ton mineral wagons on 2nd December, 1951. *Author*

met up with the 'Britannia', which was not extended by the 30-odd ton load which it then worked forward to Carlisle, and stabled at Durran Hill where we spent the weekend with final preparations. The end of January and the first half of February is not the best time of the year for weather over the Settle & Carlisle line but we were reasonably fortunate. We saw our share of snow, and on at least two occasions, when we had to stop at Blea Moor for water because of the combination of a fairly high steaming rate test and frozen troughs at Garsdale, we were able to let off steam with a snowball fight! On one of these occasions, it was a glorious day, cold and crisp, bright sunshine, clear blue skies and about six inches of fresh snow. On that day I think I came to understand what people mean when they say that the air is like wine. I have spent holidays in the area since, during high summer, and even on the best days it is not quite the same. The cold adds a crispness which is missing in the summer.

The test programme followed the same pattern that we had established over this route with the 'B1' and the Standard class '5', the test train being made up of empty coaching stock which was kept in sidings on the up side at Durran Hill, by taking as many carriages behind the dynamometer car, mobile test units and luggage van carrying the coal as was judged necessary for the steaming rates which were planned for that day's test. On return from Skipton, we stopped outside Durran Hill and 'chopped off' the coaches, which were then returned to the siding by another engine while we turned our short train ready for the next day. A similar arrangement was used at Skipton North, where we went into the up loop, and left our empty stock while we turned the short train on the triangle at Shipley, returning to Skipton where we would replenish the tender before going out to the North Junction to pick up the train again ready for our 'home' run.

As with the earlier series, I was able to get in a few 'driving turns' on the turning run to Shipley and was fortunate to drop on the ones which were particularly interesting, and taught me a thing or two into the bargain. My first trip happened to coincide with a high steam rate test, one of the ones where we had stopped at Blea Moor for water. We had left a long train behind in the sidings, and dropped our colleagues off in Skipton station to have their lunch. We had had two firemen on the test, and Joe Storey was taking the train to Shipley, while Joe Armstrong was in the car having his 'snap', and inspector Willis had also gone in there for a break. As we left Skipton Frank Dowell got the train on the move and then stood up and turned to me. 'Right-oh you can sit there and get on with it. Just don't break any records!' And he went to the locker on the tender front, took out his sandwich box and his paper, and sat down on the fireman's seat, leaving me to my own devices. So here I was, actually driving a 'Britannia'. As speed was increasing, I pulled the reverser back, pulling the rim of the wheel round and not using the handle, having seen the damage Frank did to his knuckles a day or two earlier. Having the advantage of a speedometer, I kept our speed around 60 mph, and had an uneventful run down to Shipley.

I had been on this run enough times to know my signals, and was able to come nicely to a stand over the points at Guiseley Junction. Joe was over on his side, looking for signals for the reversal, and called 'Right away for back' long before I had pulled the reverser into backgear. Watching knuckles again! In due course, I was about half way back, and opened the regulator and we moved steadily back over the junction, through the Bradford platform to come to a stand behind the 'dolly' at Bradford Junction. Then it was wind the gear forward again as quickly as possible, because the signalman had the points over almost before we had come to a stand, and had the ground disc clear seconds later! As soon as I was around 25 per cent, I cracked the regulator, a short blast on the whistle, and back to winding, as we moved off sedately. Close the regulator as we run into the platform and brake gently to a stand at the Bingley Junction starter. Joe Storey opened the door and climbed down, had a word or two with Joe Armstrong who then took his place, Joe S going to the car for his meal.

Frank was still immersed in his paper, and had not shown the slightest interest in what was happening. I was keeping an eye on the signal, having by now got the reverser well forward, and when the signal cleared, a short whistle of acknowledge, as a warning that we were moving off, and I tugged the regulator handle towards me. I also had a quick look back and responded to the wave the guard was giving, to show he was still with us! The 'Britannia' regulator seemed a bit insensitive at first, but once you got used to it, it was fine. I think possibly the 'heaviness' was due to the long rods along the boiler with their intermediate expansion link, linking the handle to the multiple valve regulator in the superheater header. There was a lot of metal to move, and I suppose the movement was unusual too, with the pivot high up in the cab roof, so that the handle moved in an arc from a vertical position, to an angle of, I am guessing, about 35° behind the vertical for full regulator.

As with the up run, I made sure that I did as Frank had told me, and did not break any records. I did take the opportunity to make good use of the glorious

Two views of ex-North Eastern Railway class 'S' (LNER class 'B13') No. 1699. This engine had been used on the LNER for counter-pressure testing and was kept at Rugby Testing Plant from 1948 to 1951, when it was scrapped. *(Both) Author*

tri-tone whistle, particularly as we came through the tunnel to Bingley station, and again at Keighley. There were also several level crossings, all of which I decided needed fair warning of our approach.

As we came towards Cononley, the distant was on, and I closed the regulator. Joe came and looked over my shoulder 'We'll be going inside, the 'Thames-Clyde' must be behind us' he said. 'Bring her down (surely *John Milton* should have been 'him'?) the bobby should have off for you into the loop. Just take it gently'. Sure enough the subsidiary signal was off and we lurched smoothly to the left into the loop line and rolled to a stand at the signal. We had probably been there for about three minutes when a 'Jubilee' came blasting past with the staccato exhaust of a three-cylinder engine. 'He stops at Skipton', said Joe, 'so we'll be a minute or two yet'. In due course, I saw the points move over, and the signal cleared immediately. Skipton was no great distance, so I did not try to build up speed, but just kept going at about 35 to 40, finally rolling to a stand at the north end of the platform, ready to take water. Frank came across and put his snap tin and paper in the locker. 'Not bad for an amateur' says he with a grin. 'I'll let you have another try'. He sat down on the seat I had vacated. Joe had gone to help the other Joe - they were filling the tank. Sandy climbed up, had a look at the fire, and gave me a nod. I never knew if he was aware of what was going on, but I think it was most likely, however, as there were never any problems (although as you will see, it was close at times), I am sure he was happy to turn Nelson's eye on the proceedings.

I had my next try a day or two later, on 11th February, 1952 to be precise. This was the day of the funeral of King George VI and I heard Sandy reminding Frank and Joe Armstrong that between certain times, 10 am and 3pm I think it was, the engine whistle must not be sounded. This day's test was at 'normal' steaming rates so Joe Storey was not with us, as it was well within the capabilities of one fireman. Consequently, there was nothing spectacular about the run, we were able to keep the tender water supply adequate by dipping the troughs at Garsdale, an activity which Joe usually left to me, as generally our test was finished by that time. I soon got the hang of it, although on my first attempt, I was too enthusiastic and Joe had to help me to wind the scoop up, against the pressure of the water. Our train was put inside at Skipton North, and Sandy climbed down, telling Frank 'I'm away for my piece', a bit unusual because he usually went back at the station. Anyway, Frank went straight away to the locker, and jerked his head at me, sitting on the fireman's seat. 'C'mon out of it, get over there'. Needless to say, I did not need to be told twice. We set off, and I brought us to a stand in the platform opposite the refreshment room. Vic Roberts looked twice when he saw me at the driver's window, and Joe leaning over the door waiting for the guard's right-away. He didn't say anything, either then or later. Another touch of Nelson's eye!

As we moved off Joe says 'You know about the whistle', and I assured him that I did, having overheard Sandy giving the instruction earlier. He then busied himself with the fire, and the injectors, while I got us going at a fair clip. Then it happened. We were doing about 65 on a long left-hand curve and I spotted two men in the four-foot walking with their backs to us. I slammed the regulator shut, took a fistful of brake, and was just reaching for the whistle when I remembered. By this time, Joe was at my elbow, and Frank was actually looking up from his paper. We were catching them up rapidly, and I remembered Holyhead and No. 43027. I wrenched the regulator wide and opened the cylinder cocks. All vision disappeared, there were several powerful beats from the chimney, as the brakes were really biting, and I closed the regulator again. I knew we must be close to where I had last seen the men, and as the steam cleared, I was relieved to see them at the side of the line no more than 20 yards away. Big Joe and I shook our fists as we passed, I released the brake and Joe called 'OK Frank, we missed 'em'. Frank came across as I opened up again - I was glad I was sitting down, as my knees felt like jelly - 'Who taught you that trick?' Frank enquired. I told him about the previous incident. 'Well', he said, 'it worked. I'd 'ave blown t'whistle, funeral or no funeral, it would've prevented two more'. We all laughed weakly. I felt quite pleased that I had not had to contravene the rule of the day. Frank had to explain why we had to brake sharply, but of course did not say who was doing what at the time. I 'saw' those two men many times after, and even today can recognise where we were, when I travel over the route.

I had several other 'driving turns' to Shipley, most of which were without incident, but the one which provided me with the most exciting run - maybe exciting is not quite the word, but I can't think of any word better - was on the last day of the series with *John Milton*, 15th February, 1952, just four days after the previous incident so as you will see, I had quite a week.

The intention was to test No. 70005 to the limit, to establish the maximum steaming rate which could be achieved. Around this time, a problem had arisen with 'Britannias' in service with driving wheels moving on the axles. For some reason, it had been decided not to fit keys and to rely purely on the press fit. As I recall, the immediate solution was to press plugs into the axle ends, the axles being bored right through in the interest of reducing weight. We had the wheels and axles on *John Milton* carefully marked and these were checked frequently throughout the tests. Despite the prodigious power which we extracted from the locomotive, we had no problem, I am pleased to say. We had Joe Storey with us on this memorable Friday, and the train which had been marshalled in Durran Hill Sidings seemed to disappear into the distance as we stood alongside the engine, with the dynamometer car, two mobile test units and the luggage van with coal for return run, followed by no fewer than 20 coaches. The total weight was 730 tons, and with the MTUs in use, this could be equivalent to approximately 850 tons. The tail lamp was well over a quarter of a mile behind us. Joe Armstrong had built up a good fire ready for our departure, and we brought a few bags out of the van to ensure the tender was completely full. The intention was to take this monstrous train over Ais Gill, and then to leave the 20 coaches in the yard at Settle station - the siding at Skipton North was not long enough for us to go inside and leave them there. We were going to bring the four vehicles which we worked to Shipley back as our train for the return run, which was going to be a low steaming rate.

Departure time came, and Joe had timed it very well, with the needle just below the blowing off point, a good thick fire which would soon burn the green coal off the top and the water well up in the glass. I think all of us on the footplate that morning, including the two lads in the tender, realised that we were in for something special. Our signal went to clear, the flash of the guard's green flag could just be distinguished in response to the blast on the whistle. Frank had already got the gear well forward, although he was not quite in full gear. He had put sand down as we backed down on to the train, and as he opened the regulator, *John Milton* almost seemed to shudder as the load came on to the drawbar. We began to move forward slowly, with our exhaust seeming to explode from the chimney in clear cut beats. Speed seemed to build up slowly, and our ponderous departure was watched by a group of men standing outside the locomotive shed. Later on that day, the foreman told me that we could still be heard 15 minutes after the last vehicle disappeared through the bridge just beyond the shed.

I had set the manometer pointer on the slave instrument at Frank's left elbow. Once we were past Cotehill, where there was a short downhill stretch past Low House crossing, we started on the test in earnest. Frank had got the regulator full open, and as he advanced the reverser, the mercury level rose in the tube until it was opposite the pointer. I told Ernest that we were at the set position, so that we could make a final check alongside the master equipment in the car. Occasionally we found that the settings required minor adjustments, but today we were spot-on. The two Joe's were hard at work, working as a team, each man firing five hundredweights of coal, and then passing over the shovel, and taking his place working the firedoors. This was essential at high steam outputs to minimise the inflow of cold air through the firehole. I think it also kept some of the white-heat out of the cab. If the doors had been open all the time, we should have all been 'done to a turn'.

As the test settled down the hundredweights were following one another into the furnace every 50 seconds! Not only were Joe and Joe sweating at their efforts, but the coal-men were only just about able to keep the coal-plate fed with fuel. At one stage, Frank distracted Joe Storey momentarily and he did not open the firedoors on cue, and poor Joe Armstrong crashed a full shovel into them. Coal spewed all over the place, and Joe Storey had to pick up the shovel, as Joe A could not carry on. Sandy sat him on the fireman's seat, and took over on the doors. Joe S stuck it as long as he could, then Sandy fired about three bags, Joe A took over the doors again as the numbness was going out of his forearms, Joe S did five or six, then Joe A took the shovel off him and the rhythm was restored.

We were pounding along in fine style - I can't remember all the speeds and corresponding cut-offs, but in the vicinity of Lazonby, we were doing just over 70 mph and the cut-off was 40 per cent! It was quite incredible, and as we got on to the 1 in 100 south of Appleby towards Griseburn Box, our speed fell off and the exhaust beats came louder and clearer. According to my records, we had the gear as far forward as 59 per cent, with a corresponding speed of 32 mph, at one stage. Sandy was keeping an eye on the tender water gauge, which was of course falling quite rapidly, as both injectors were on, and he decided that we were not going to reach Blea Moor, or even Garsdale, and we would have to stop at Kirkby Stephen for water! Forty-one miles to use most of the contents of a 4,250 gallon tank. The steam rate which we achieved was 3,615 gallons per hour, and the coal rate was 5,600 pounds per hour - 2½ tons in 60

BR Standard 'Britannia' class 4-6-2 No. 70005 *John Milton* taking water at Blea Moor on 4th February, 1952. The train consist of No. 1 Dynamometer Car, Mobile Test Units Nos. 2 and 3, a luggage van carrying coal for the return run and seven bogie coaches. *Author*

minutes! Looking back on the day's events, I consider that I was very fortunate - nay, even privileged! - to be on the footplate during what must have been one of the most outstanding efforts by a 'Britannia' of all time . . . I know that *John Milton* produced even higher figures on the Rugby Test Plant, but there speeds were constant, cut-off was constant, the driver was 'minding' rather than actually driving and the test duration was usually relatively short. Also the supply of fuel was easier and there was no limit on the water supply.

With the tank replenished, *John Milton* heaved the train into motion again and we blasted our way up past Mallerstang to the summit at Ais Gill, roared across the moors towards Garsdale with Frank giving his usual salute on the whistle to the lady in one of the cottages near Moorcock tunnel, for which he came across the cab in this direction. In all my trips with him, I don't think there were as many times as could be counted on the fingers of one hand when there was no response from the cottage doorway. Goodness knows when she went shopping!

We put the train into Settle station yard, no small feat in itself when the guard is so far away, and we had to split the train to stow it on two roads, and the gradient is against the engine too. Vic Roberts had a look at the wheels and pronounced himself satisfied. Then off we went with our much reduced train, and in due course, drew up in Skipton platform. The now familiar routine, Sandy and Joe Armstrong climbed down, Frank stood up and pointed to the seat while looking at me and away we went. Quite a straightforward run to Shipley as far as I was concerned, *John Milton* showing no signs of the hard work to which he had been subjected. Everything went smoothly at Shipley, as by now I had perfected a sort of hand-over-hand technique for pulling the reverser back by the wheel rim, and using the handle when going into fore gear, pushing the handle with an open hand rather than fingers gripped round it, at the crucial knucklebarking position. So we came to the Bingley Junction starter and Joe A took the place of Joe S. Away we went, and in a short time I was sort of half aware that Joe was not firing and had opened the tender front doors. As we were running through Bingley station, he spoke to Frank, and then came across to me. 'Come and look at this' and he pointed into the tender. I stood up and looked into the coal space. The sight that met my eyes made my blood run cold! Joe had swept all the coal into a heap and it formed a rough cone probably about three feet round and certainly no higher. Perhaps 10 shovelfuls at the most. 'Aye-up Frank' says I, 'I think you'd better take over'. 'Not bloody likely, you got us into this mess, so you can get us out', was the response.

I went back to the driving seat and pulled the gear back to about 10 per cent, closed the regulator, and opened it to about a quarter, which gave me 80 lb. in the steam chest. Frank came across. 'No', he said, 'set it about 35 or 40, and then give her full regulator up to about 60 mph and then coast'. He put his sandwich tin and paper away, and came and stood by me, but refused to take the seat! Joe, meanwhile, had turned the steam heater off and kept peering into the fire, eyeing the water gauge, and glancing at the pressure gauge. I could not see the fire, but the other two were going down! Frank said, 'Let's hope the 'Thames-Clyde' is late today'. I knew what he meant, because as with the Monday run mentioned earlier, every day that week our return run had involved going into the loop at Cononley. If that happened today, we would be struggling along the ballast with bags of coal, whereas if we ran straight to Skipton, it would be much easier in the platform. So we were all anxiously looking for the Cononley distant. Joe got the first glimpse 'It's off', he shouted, and Frank said, 'OK Alan, give it a go'. I opened up for a final spurt to give us a run which should take us into Skipton. Joe put two shovelfuls of coal into the box and said, 'That's the lot'. We ran into the platform and I pulled us up by the water column. Joe shouted to the test crew standing on the platform to get some coal as quickly as possible and they grabbed a platform barrow and we soon had half a dozen bags on the footplate. There was still some red patches in the fire, on to which Joe carefully placed fresh coal. The pressure was down to 160 lb., and if you stood on tiptoe, you could see water in the bottom nut! Sandy had joined us and said that the 'Thames-Clyde' was over half an hour late. I suspect that my guardian angel must have had a hand in that. So it was that in about 20 minutes, we had a bright, if thin, fire, a quarter of a glass of water, and the tender tank filled.

We were able to move across to the Ilkley line down platform to load the tender, and I was breathing normally again. I did not enjoy it at the time, but looking over my shoulder these days, it is one of the highlights in my Testing career.

The run home to Carlisle was reasonably uneventful, although the engine was not steaming properly, as part of the brick arch fell into the fire, and we subsequently found that there was some damage to the piston valve heads, discovered when the engine was examined at Crewe works. This run was an anticlimax, anyway, after the morning's performance, and I think we were all glad when we reached Durran Hill and put the train away.

To this day, I often wonder why Joe Storey did not say something to Frank or myself, so we could have brought some coal forward at Shipley. Even Joe Armstrong could have suggested it. They both must have known the position, but I suppose if either of them had done so, it would have spoilt my story. So I am glad they didn't!

Above: Ex-WD 2-8-0 No. 90464 at Dumfries up platform, taking water before continuing to Carlisle in April 1952. *Author*

Right: The Selsyn drive unit with Hookes coupling fitted to 'Austerity' 2-8-0 No. 90464. This ensures that the Farnborough Indicator rotates in sync with the driving wheels. *P. Baker*

Chapter Nine

The Farnborough Indicator

The week after the tests with *John Milton*, I was off to Rugby again, this time to oversee the preparations of the Standard class '5' No. 73008. In those days, there was still a line across country from Leicester to Rugby, and from my notes I see that I went to Rugby by that route, but I always came back home via Birmingham. We took the '5' to Carlisle on Thursday 28th February, and I spent the following Sunday in Newcastle, visiting places like Tyne Dock and Percy Main! I think Gateshead and Heaton were also on the itinerary.

We had a week with No. 73008 on this occasion, as it was a follow-up to the 1951 series, with the engine having run up service mileage in between. It was really a series of checks to see if there was any marked change in performance as mileage was accumulated. I managed a couple of Shipley turns in the week, but without any of the excitement of my previous journeys over the line. I always enjoyed my rides on No. 73008, and other engines of the class, they always seemed to give a steady ride, and I never experienced the awful banging and thumping on one of these that was so typical of an LMS 'Black Five' when they had run a good mileage, and had developed a lot of 'slop' in the trailing axleboxes.

Towards the end of March, we were back in Carlisle again, but this time our test route was to be North over the border, along the Glasgow & South Western to Hurlford, on the outskirts of Kilmarnock. The form of the tests was to be different too, as whereas over the Midland line we worked the engine at a constant steaming rate, in these tests we were going to control the speed at a constant figure, using the mobile test units. In fact, in the course of one return run, it was intended to carry out several tests at different speeds, as it was considered that a test period of 30 to 35 minutes was adequate. The measurements for these tests were much more comprehensive than for the constant steam rate tests.

The mobile test plant at this time was still operated by the Research Department but the intention was that it would be taken over by the Mechanical Engineers' Department, and this series of test was 'double manned' for training purposes. The engine which was 'guinea pig' was one of the ex-WD 2-8-0 'Austerity' locomotives, No. 90464. As I said earlier, the instrumentation was very comprehensive with full smokebox gas analysis, the thermocouples to measure temperatures in both firebox and smokebox, a weighing grate which monitored the weight of the grate and fire constantly, and also indicator elements in the cylinder covers so that indicator diagrams could be taken by means of the Farnborough indicator in the dynamometer car.

I was to become familiar with both the indicator equipment and the weighing grate in quite intimate detail, in the next few weeks. I had been selected to learn to operate the indicator, being taught by Pat Larkham who was one of Dr Andrews' Research Department team who had manned the mobile test plant in the past. I already had some knowledge of the equipment, and in particular I

The front cylinder cover of WD 2-8-0 No. 90464 showing the indicator element with air and electrical connections. *P. Baker*

The Farnborough Indicator installed in No. 3 Dynamometer Car in April 1952. *Author*

had had to draw up the arrangement drawing of the drive unit which was fitted on to the locomotive and which was driven off one of the crankpins by an arm attached to the crankpin nut. This arm was towards the axle centre line, and carried two driving pins which described a circle round that centre line as the wheelset rotated. The pins were engaged in blocks which could slide along guides in a Hookes coupling, the disc having another pair of guides at right angles, to form a cruciform layout. These second pair of guides slid on two more blocks which in turn were attached to a driving bevel gear, which rotated a bevel pinion and so drove a Selsyn generator, if memory serves me right, at four times the speed of the driving wheels. This Selsyn unit was coupled electrically to a Selsyn motor which drove the recording cylinder of the indicator through a step down gear ratio the same as the bevel ratio mentioned earlier, so that the cylinder rotated at the same speed as the driving wheels.

As the Hookes coupling was placed with the cruciform member in a vertical plane and parallel to the driving wheel, it was able to take account of the rise and fall of the axleboxes, and as the pins drove blocks which also incorporated a ball and socket arrangement, tilt of the axle was also allowed for. The drive unit was usually suspended on angle sections from the footplating and care had to be taken to place it at the correct distance from the lazy crank, otherwise the pins would go too far into the Hookes coupling with disastrous results, or else would come out of the blocks, with equally damaging consequences when the wheel set moved back again!

In use, a Farnborough indicator operates in a rather different manner to the Dobbie McInnes type with which steam engineers are more familiar. The Farnborough was developed at the Royal Aeronautical Establishment for in-flight indicating of aircraft engines, again positioned remotely from the engine. It produces a diagram which is an average over a short period, rather than the almost instantaneous record produced by the McInnes device. I shall have more to say about the latter in a later chapter.

The Farnborough indicator records its diagram by punching a series of holes through the paper by means of an electric spark. The spark is induced by the indicator element in the cylinder cover when a contact is broken and remade. The element is in itself a small cylinder with a tight fitting piston, one end being open to the locomotive cylinder, while the other end contains the electrical contact and a feed connection from a compressed air source. In operation, air is fed to the element from which the diagram is to be taken, to a pressure above the steam chest pressure. The air then leaks away through a bleed valve controlled by the indicator operator, and as the pressure falls below the pressure in the locomotive cylinder, the small piston moves across, breaking and making the circuit, and so producing the spark. In producing one diagram there would be several hundred sparks produced. It was also possible to put lines on the diagram to give pressures at every 50 psi. One diagram might take one or two minutes to produce, and of course, on No. 90464, there were two cylinders, each with two ends, so the whole process of indicating the engine could take several minutes.

In practice, the biggest job was maintaining the indicator elements. The electrical contact was insulated within the element body with rings of mica, and

Right: The later pattern indicator element fitted to the back cylinder cover of WD 2-8-0 No. 90464.
P. Baker

Below: The vacuum, pressure and temperature panel in No. 3 Dynamometer Car with the main control desk in the foreground.
P. Baker

the electrical connection was made with a modified miniature sparking plug. The moving contact unit was screwed on to the end of the piston at one side and, at the other, had a spring wire connection to ensure electrical continuity, as the piston to cylinder path was not reliable due to oiling. Problems arose with breakdown of the mica insulation in the presence of oil and water, and the spring wire connection was also a source of trouble. The pistons also had a nasty habit of coming unscrewed from the contact element and although there was a retaining bar about 1/16 in. diameter across the element cylinder, pistons were known to chop through that. Some disappeared, some were found in the locomotive cylinder, or in the cylinder cocks, needless to say they were not re-usable! I often think that with the development of modern materials, such as Loctite, this element design could have been made much more reliable. However, we managed to overcome a lot of the problems at the time, and usually managed to record enough diagrams for each test, even if it meant that the following day we virtually had to rebuild all the elements which we carried.

The route from Carlisle was to Gretna Junction and then along the Solway Firth through Annan to Dumfries where we took water. Then on past Thornhill, Sanquhar, New Cumnock and Mauchline to Hurlford. There must have been a triangle there for us to turn the train although I cannot recall the details of the manoeuvre, apart from it calling for an engine on the rear of the train. Servicing, watering and loading coal was carried out in Hurlford Loco Yard, before we retraced our path to Carlisle.

I had, of course, been deposed from the footplate, my place being taken by Pat Webb, and Walter King on occasions. Nevertheless, as we were using the corridor tender, and when I had finished my quota of diagrams (or run out of usable elements!), I would go through to the footplate; interesting it was too at times. On the long downhill stretches when the locomotive was not under steam - sometimes of course, the MTUs were use to hold it back so it could be pulling - the well-known 'Austerity' characteristic of 'shuttling' between engine and tender would be displayed. Under certain conditions with some engines, this could become quite severe, shaking a mountain of coal on to the footplate, and rattling the fire-irons out of their tunnel. It was not unknown for the tender hand brake to be screwed down hard to alleviate the problem, not always with success. It took me back to the analysis of the Interchange charts where the Great Western '28XX' class 2-8-0 locomotive produced a drawbar pull 'line' at certain speeds which might fluctuate by four or five tons, from say two tons to six tons, putting a broad band of ink along the chart. With the 'Austerity', the engine-tender drawgear was blamed, and it is possible that the intermediate buffer springs might have had a tendency to react with the fore-and-aft forces from the engine and amplify them. There would be no damping of any sort on the (coil) springs to counteract the effect. It was certainly quite a novel experience, and of course it must have been caused by the engine, as here we had the phenomenon with the corridor tender, not the normal 'Austerity' pattern. By all accounts from footplatemen the problem was even worse with the normal combination.

These tests were a fairly leisurely affair, inasmuch as runs were made on Mondays, Wednesdays and Fridays, with stand-down days between - useful for

An unusual view of 'Austerity' 2-10-0 No. 90772 standing at Dumfries. The junction box and pipework carrying tubes and cables associated with the test work is quite prominent, June 1952.
Author

Ex-WD 2-10-0 No. 90772 with the mobile test plant on a Carlisle to Hurlford test run at Dumfries in June 1952.
Author

repairing indicator elements! However, it did mean that some of us had to stay in Carlisle at week-ends so that all would be ready on Monday morning. Naturally, the day of work was Sunday (double time!) so that Saturday was free. One Saturday was put to good use travelling to Penrith, on to Darlington via Barnard Castle, then Middlesbrough, Sunderland to Newcastle, and back to Carlisle, while another started off the same, but from Penrith I went via Keswick to Workington, and Whitehaven, and then back to Carlisle. As you may have guessed, I like travelling by train!

This series of trials, while only running three days per week, extended from 24th March through to the 7th May. It was during this time that I applied for a job in the Research Department, in fact, the post my tutor on the Farnborough indicator was leaving. In many ways, I was sorry to even consider leaving the locomotive testing section, but after 3½ years, I was still 'temporary' and there was no sign of being put on the permanent staff. I was told that my application had been successful just before the end of the tests with No. 90464, and that I would have to be available for the next series of tests with the 2-10-0 'Austerity', No. 90772. I was to look after the self-weighing grate, and also teach Walter King to use the indicator. There was a fortnight between the tests, during which I moved into the building next door, and met my new colleagues, although I knew quite a few of them already. Then it was off to Carlisle again, to make the close acquaintance of the 2-10-0.

As with the smaller engine, No. 90772 was fully instrumented, also being paired with the corridor tender. I cannot recall a great deal of trouble with the water meter on these runs, but Basil Watson and I had spent a lot of time with this after the Willesden runs, carefully shaving high spots off the rotating member, which, combined with the tank having been swilled out, improved the reliability of the meter.

My main concern in these tests was the self-weighing grate. The grate was built up in the usual way with firebar elements, but was constructed on a frame which was supported on four weighing elements secured to the foundation ring. The elements each contained a weighbar, these being a small aluminium rod, about 5⁄16 in. diameter and 1½ in. long, the ends being slightly domed to fit in their housing. The weighbar was wound with resistance wire, only a few thousandths of an inch in diameter, leaving perhaps ¼ in. bare at the ends. The bars functioned by increasing very slightly in diameter as they were compressed, which in turn stretched the resistance wire, altering its resistance sufficiently so that when incorporated in a Wheatstone bridge there was sufficient signal to show, after calibration, a change of weight. The system was sufficiently sensitive to show the individual shovelfuls falling on the fire. Unfortunately, the electronic equipment associated with the system suffered from 'drift' of the datum. In the short term this could be ignored, and the couple of hundredweights of brick arch blocks were recorded accurately when flung through the firehole. We only did this at the end of the day, of course, as a pile of firebricks in the fire does not help steaming! However, on occasions the 'drift' factor grossly distorted the weight so that it suggested that the firebed had either increased drastically, or alternatively the fire should have almost disappeared, when the test period was 30 or 40 minutes long. Some days, it behaved reasonably well, and corresponded with the guesstimated change of weight which the footplate crew estimated had taken place. To assist in this, we had a fire-iron with a vertical spike which could be stuck down into the fire, and made it easier to tell how deep the bed was.

So much for the system. My involvement on test days was to make readings at frequent intervals and plot the points on a graph. It was on the non-running days that the hardest part occurred, and this was checking that the frame supporting the grate was able to move freely. If cinders or clinker became jammed between the frame and the firebox wall, this could affect the behaviour and accuracy of the readings. As you will have guessed, clearing the debris could only be done from inside the firebox and even when the fire has been dropped about 15 hours previously, it was still very hot therein. However, it only took about 1¼ hours, or maybe a little longer, even when I had to clean the firebox pyrometer which was positioned above the brick arch and fairly close to the tubeplate. As I was no longer under the eagle eye of Vic Roberts, and was more or less left to my own devices, I tended to lie a-bed a little, have a leisurely breakfast (timing my entrance to the canteen to be just as the other lads were leaving), and then make my way down to Durran Hill. If there were any elements to be worked on, I gave a hand, and then changed ready for my stint. Changed is hardly the word, as it was a case of underpants, boots, a boiler suit, the legs tucked into socks, elastic bands round the wrists, an old pair of gloves, a scarf wrapped tightly round my neck with the boiler suit buttoned right up and an old balaclava helmet to complete the outfit. Not the height of sartorial elegance, it must be admitted, and at first sight designed to combat cold, not heat! However, bare metal in that firebox was uncomfortably hot, so the less bare skin there was, the better.

I climbed on the footplate with a hand lamp, and then knelt facing the tender, inserting first one foot and leg, then the other into the firehole. Wriggling backwards, with my arms straight out above my head towards the end, I was soon kneeling in the firebox. I usually took a piece of board in with me, as firebars are not kind to knees. Finally, reaching out for the lamp, I would then start to work round the grate to poke out the ashes, cinders and clinker. Sometimes, the firegrate elements had to be lifted out, and then replaced. When I was satisfied, and after attention to the pyrometer, I would crawl out head-first onto the footplate, wringing wet of course. The scheme was then to discard gloves, balaclava, scarf and change the boots for shoes, put on an overcoat, and a brisk walk back to Upperby hostel. I sometimes wonder what folks thought as I passed, wearing an overcoat in June and July! Then a long hot bath, a change into clean clothes, and it was lunchtime. I usually went down to Durran Hill for a bit in the afternoons, although on some occasions, I was able to get in a firing turn to Whitehaven and back.

This came about because there were a couple of drivers resident at Upperby. Unfortunately, I can't remember their names, one came from Rose Grove (Burnley) and the other from Dallam (Warrington) on temporary, but long-term, loan. We got to know them quite well, as they were often in the recreation room in the evening when we came in. I met the Rose Grove man one day just after I had had my bath, and happened to mention that I was finished for the day. He was just going on duty, and suggested that if I would like to, I could go to Whitehaven with him. I accepted at once, and we walked down to the shed, where I was introduced to his fireman. We found our engine, an LMS 'Black Five', and backed down to Citadel station in due course and coupled to our train, which was a stopping passenger to Whitehaven. We had an uneventful journey, during which I was invited to take the shovel several times.

On arrival at Whitehaven, we uncoupled, took the engine to the turntable and turned it, filled the tank, pulled some coal down and then screwed down on a siding, as we had about an hour and a half before our return working. We went off into the town and down near the harbour I was taken into a tiny bar where we had a couple of rounds. It was about four in the afternoon, but it did not seem to matter. Feeling rested, we returned to our steed, livened up the fire, and the boiler and, at the appointed hour, shunted into the station, and coupled to our coaches, which had been moved into the down platform by the station pilot.

When we were ready, the driver said 'How'd you like to fire us home?' I replied that that was fine with me, and then he told the fireman that he could go and ride in the train! I had not bargained for that, but I was not too bothered. I had quite an enjoyable run, and even had time to look out over the sea at Harrington. The fireman looked out at Workington, and the driver gave him the thumbs-up, so he disappeared again. I got it a bit wrong at Maryport and was making more smoke than I should have been, but that was soon rectified, except that then the safety valves lifted. Fortunately, there was room for water in the boiler, so putting the injector on soon quietened things down. By and large, I was quite pleased with my handling of the firing duties, and the driver was good enough to say that I had done 'all right'. The fireman came back at Dalston, to avoid any awkward questions if he was seen to alight from the train on arrival at Citadel.

Various landmarks were pointed out to me *en route* and one particular one led to another excursion. This was the Bullgill distant coming from Maryport, which was perched high up on the hill side above the line. I went out one afternoon to take a photograph of it at close quarters. There it stood, surrounded by bracken and undergrowth, with no sign of a railway line, until you looked down to where the trains ran some hundred feet below. It must have been the lampman's nightmare.

I was also able to have a trip over the Waverley route one weekend when I did not come home. If my memory serves me right, the 'A3' *Captain Cuttle* was our head-end power for the run through Hawick, St Boswells and Galasheils to Edinburgh. I can't remember the engine number for the return run, but it was a 'V2'. Edinburgh, of course, meant Haymarket and St Margaret's with a wealth of locomotive classes from 'A4s' right down to the diminutive 'Y9' 0-4-0 'Pugs' such as No. 8093 which was 'on shed' that day. I also had time to go to Dalry Road where the biggest engine to be seen was a Compound. Today, of course, the Waverley Route is no more and the countryside it traversed is a railway wilderness, despite the efforts of the Border Union Railway Group whose schemes, unfortunately, came to naught.

I seem to have got diverted more than somewhat from No. 90772! Like the previous series, these tests covered a long period, from late May to mid-July. I

Above: Bullgill distant signal, between Whitehaven and Carlisle. This signal was on a hillside about 120 feet above the railway line, in the valley at left of signal post foot. *Author*

Right: A view over WD 2-10-0 No. 90772 standing on the down line at Dumfries in June 1952. *Author*

cannot recall anything remarkable about them, and of course, I was no longer the footplate observer. However, as with No. 90464, I spent a fair time on the footplate, and I was even able to obtain some photographs looking ahead over the locomotive by climbing up inside the tender. There were some problems with No. 90772 with some of the coal that was being used, which soon formed a mass of clinker and we had to change to a different grade. Whether this was due to the different grate on the 2-10-0, with the wide firebox, I don't know, but the narrow firebox on the 2-8-0 did not seem to cause trouble. One difference that was welcome was that the 2-10-0 did not display the unpleasant fore-and-aft shuttling which made the smaller engine rather unpleasant to ride on at times.

To a certain extent, No. 90772 was my 'swan-song' as far as steam locomotive testing was concerned. The Research Department were, in fact, bowing out of that field, so that in some ways I was to find that I had burned my boats by moving. However, I still had a considerable involvement with steam locomotives and was able to indulge in footplate trips on quite a few occasions, as we shall see in the remaining chapters.

I don't think there were ever any more comprehensive tests than those with Nos. 90464 and 90772. The weighing grate was never used again and I don't think that much use was made of the Farnborough indicator either. I know my ex-colleagues had some interesting runs between Carlisle and Skipton with a 'Merchant Navy' after I left them which I am sure I would have enjoyed, but on balance, I am glad I made the change. Much of what followed was quite different, but still involved the steam engine, which had now been the centre of my working life for 10 years, and by which I remain bewitched to this day.

A view looking ahead over the top of ex-WD 2-10-0 No. 90772 approaching Thornhill up distant signal with a test run from Hurlford to Carlisle in June 1952. *Author*

Chapter Ten

Axleboxes, Boilers and Brakes

After the completion of the tests with No. 90772, the remainder of 1952 was taken up by finding my feet in the Research Department where my group leader was Tom Rhead. I spent a lot of time doing tests on wagon axleboxes, which at that time were a considerable problem, and we had been asked to try to come up with a solution to the hot-box. At the time there were basically two types of axlebox, the fabricated pattern made by welding up pieces of steel, and the cast-iron split box, with a horizontal dividing face. I was involved in a series of wind tunnel tests, in which an electric heater was placed in the box, and surface temperatures measured to determine the heat dissipation characteristics of the various axlebox designs.

Having determined that the cast-iron box took the heat away from the bearing much more efficiently, it was felt that some running tests would be helpful, with thermocouples embedded in the bearings, to monitor the temperatures. My chief decided that most of the heat arose at the bearing ends, with relatively high loads being taken by the outer end collar, and the radius at the wheel end of the journal. I was asked to think about means of supplementing the lubrication, particularly at the outer end of the journal. The normal lubrication was by means of a worsted pad, soaked in oil, and fed by wicks from the reservoir in the bottom half of the box. My scheme was a bit 'Heath Robinson' and consisted of a gear pump driven by a 'surplus' 24 volt electric motor, taking oil from the reservoir, and feeding it through a pair of nozzles to be squirted on to the end of the bearing, and the journal collar. The pump could only be run for 15 to 20 seconds before it emptied the reservoir, but of course, the oil soon drained back for another squirt. Tom approved of the idea, and a pair of boxes were fitted to one of the test wagons.

My views were sought on a suitable route for the trials, and in March 1953 we set off for Carlisle with a fortnight's running to Hurlford and back. One minor change was that we were based at Kingmoor instead of Durran Hill, and lodged in the Kingmoor hostel. Our train was hauled by a class '5' each day, and I was able to enjoy one or two spells on the footplate, as well as taking the opportunity to ride over the Leeds to Carlisle stretch when we took the test train out, and again on the way back. It was a change to be able to watch the scenery instead of being intent on boiler pressure, water level and all the other items that had to be watched on the earlier tests over the line.

For some reason that I can no longer remember, I seemed to stop taking photographs when out on tests. I know that around this time I was experimenting with Dufay Color film and so did not take so many pictures because of the expense. I went on a couple of enthusiasts specials in April and May, one over the Cromford & High Peak Railway (C&HP) and the other over the Midland & South Western Junction (MSWJ) between Cheltenham and Andover, the latter being behind the MSWJ 2-4-0 No. 1336. The CH&P was a particular favourite of mine, and I have spent many years, both before and after closure, studying the line.

In June, I was involved in a brief series of measurements on service trains between Euston and Wolverhampton. I cannot recall the details now but my share was to provide a colleague with locations, such as mileposts, stations, etc. throughout the journey. These were the well known 'Two Hour' expresses, worked by Bushbury 'Jubilees', over the 125¾ miles stopping at Birmingham and Coventry. I usually had a chat with the engine crews, and one driver's comment when I asked him if it was difficult to keep time was that you could do it if you only shut the regulator at the platform end at Euston!

This job gave me an opportunity to go to London over the Great Central from Nottingham to Marylebone, prior to picking up the first run from Euston, and was the first of several occasions when I forsook the St Pancras route in favour of an alternative. Although British Railways had been one entity for over five years, nevertheless the pre-nationalisation railways were still distinguishable, and this run was very much an LNER occasion, with a Gresley 'A3' Pacific hauling a rake of Gresley coaches.

As readers will see, the involvement with the steam locomotive had diminished quite considerably, and it was no more than the power at the head of the train. And so it was very pleasant to find that the next job was to involve riding on the footplate and also that Tom was going to be around for a day or two, and then leave me to carry on.

The subject of our endeavours was the LNER 'N2' 0-6-2T engine designed by Gresley for suburban work. One or two members of the class had become derailed when working trains, one near Bathgate in Scotland and another in the East Midlands, and the Research Department had been asked if they could investigate the problem. The test route we used was based at Hatfield, running on the cross-country single line from Welwyn Garden City to Luton and Dunstable. Initially, I was expected to ride on the 'N2' engines shedded at Hatfield and working to Dunstable, so that I became familiar with the riding characteristics, and I was also told to have some 'Main Line' runs up to the Cross to observe their behaviour at speed. The shedmaster at Hatfield, Bill Cattermole, was most helpful, and I was accompanied by a Kings Cross locomotive inspector whose name now escapes me. The three of us were all motorcycle sidecar men, Bill having a Square Four Ariel, the inspector being a Panther enthusiast, while I ran a 500 cc BSA. We had some yarns and arguments about our various mounts. The inspector only came along on the branch, leaving me to my own devices on my other excursions up to Kings Cross, and across to Hertford North.

I also had one or two turns on the ex-GE designed 'N7' engines, which were included in the Hatfield stud. They were quite a good riding engine, and did not display the rough riding which the 'N2s' were prone to. The Dunstable line abounded in curves, some of which were quite sharp, and the 'N2' would go round these in a series of jerks with the front end lurching sideways rather than progressing smoothly. All engines worked chimney first to Dunstable normally, but I was able to have one turned round to see what difference it made. I should have known - we simply got the rough ride coming home! Out on the main line, the behaviour was quite different, and a relatively smooth ride was the order of the day, at speeds up to the sixties. Obviously some engines that I rode on were in need of works attention, but account was made for this, as Bill was able to

'N2' class 0-6-2T No. 69542 on a Hertford train at Kings Cross. I covered many miles between Hatfield and Dunstable on Nos. 69579 and 69580 in the course of trials to improve the riding of the class between 1953 and 1955. *Author*

'A3' class 4-6-2 No. 60076 *Galopin* at Gateshead on 2nd March, 1952. I had a day out on 16th July, 1953 and rode on No. 60053 *Sansovino* from Grantham to Kings Cross, and returned on No. 60106 *Flying Fox*. Superb! *Author*

find out mileages since shopping, either from his shed records, or by picking up the phone if I had ridden on a Kings Cross or Stratford engine.

In my first week, I clocked up about 500 miles on the footplates of various engines. Going to London for another spell, I went from Friargate station to Grantham, and from there to Kings Cross rode on No. 60114 *W.P. Allen*. I was rather surprised by the riding which was rough to say the least, and not what I would have expected from a Pacific, particularly as this was a relatively modern design. I also rode on No. 60144 *Kings Courier* on another occasion over the same route, and was again impressed only by the poor behaviour. The latter trip, I remember, was the occasion when, negotiating a curve, the fallplate between engine and tender trapped the sole of my boot for several seconds, as I was standing on the tender rather than the engine. Fortunately, no damage was done, either to the boot or me, but I moved on to the footplate proper and hung on to the handrail for the rest of the journey!

At the end of the week, I decided to come home via Grantham, and make full use of the Eastern Region footplate pass. So on Friday afternoon, I made my way up to Kings Cross, and was delighted to find an 'A4' No. 60015 *Quicksilver* at the head of my train. I was made welcome by the crew, and the fireman sat me in the comfort of his upholstered seat - what a difference from the wooden flip-up effort on a Stanier 'Pacific'. I had a most enjoyable trip, a world of difference from the up run on Monday previous, with an engine which was as smooth as silk by comparison. I had a go with the shovel too, but I found the Gresley firedoor difficult, so I was not too successful. I was used to the gaping maw of the Stanier engines which had re-appeared on the BR Standards as well, so that the oval LNER pattern, with the built in flap, seemed like feeding coal through a letter-box! Grantham came all too soon, and I bade farewell to the driver and his mate, and spent most of the rest of the journey home trying to clean myself up.

The following week was a 'short' one, going to London on Tuesday, and having a couple of Dunstable trips on Wednesday, coming home the same night. On the Thursday, I took a day's leave, and made further use of the pass, going across to Grantham, then riding up on No. 60053 *Sansovino*, and down on No. 60106 *Flying Fox*. It was a beautiful sunny day, and both engine crews made me welcome, and were particularly interested in the 'N2' work. I was able to get in a bit more firing experience - it was rare to find a fireman who would not hand over the shovel for a spell - and I managed to cope rather better with the firedoor on these occasions, by watching carefully how the fireman wielded the shovel before I volunteered for a spell! Unfortunately, I did not make a note of the drivers' names. One thing I did note, however, was the excellent riding of both of these 'A3' engines.

An approach from the Mechanical Engineer's Department to develop a gradient indicator produced a series of tests in October and November. The gradient device was required to give an instant reading of the slope of the line which the train was traversing. It was only for use on test trains where the speed was held constant by the mobile test plant, as any acceleration or deceleration would affect the bubble in the instrument and falsify the reading. Tom Rhead discussed how we were going to tackle the problem, and he was able to obtain

Ex-LMS class '5' 4-6-0 No. 44738 with Caprotti valve gear, fitted for the indicator tests, with No. 1 Dynamometer Car, standing near English Bridge Junction at Shrewsbury, ready to return to Crewe on 1st October, 1953. *P. Baker*

The drop arm to provide drive to the indicator drum on the Dobie-Mcinnes indicator on No. 44738 on 1st October, 1953. *P. Baker*

Doorway on to indicator shelter showing selector steam valve to feed steam from front or back of the cylinder to indicator on No. 44738 on 1st October, 1953. *P. Baker*

a couple of spirit level 'bubbles', one a 'quick' one with a low viscosity liquid, while the other was rather 'slower'. The bubble tubes were to be mounted on a table which was hinged at one end, and elevated at the other end by a screw. Tom wanted a fine thread and I was able to produce 40 thread taps and die so that we were able to calibrate the elevating wheel very easily. I lashed up the 'prototype' with Meccano parts and the 40 thread screw and nut, and then we made a more sophisticated model in the workshop.

Armed with this device, I joined the test train which was going to Crewe to carry out a series of tests with LMS class '4' 'Big Goods' 0-6-0 engines. This series was designed to evaluate boiler tubes which were manufactured to provide several longitudinal ribs with a slight screw or 'rifling' on the inside of the tube, intended to promote a swirl to the flue gases, so that the contact with the tube wall would be improved with better heat transfer. The tubes were covered by a patent and rejoiced in the name of Swirlyflo.

Two engines were involved, No. 44203 with the Swirlyflo tubes and No. 44030 which was the standard for comparison. The tests were between Crewe and Holyhead, and involved the dynamometer car and mobile test units. The route was useful for gradient tests, as there were quite a lot of level stretches, as well as the sharp climb from Abergele to Penmaenrhos tunnel, and the corresponding pitch from Colwyn Bay in the up direction. It was a very pleasant time for me with former colleagues and we had a lot of spare time at Holyhead in the afternoons, although as it was October and November, the darkness fell in early evening. We also had spare time at the Crewe end but, of course, the scenic delights in the area are rather less! However, I did have the opportunity to fill some of this time in a very entertaining and instructive way.

The Locomotive Testing Section, as well as conducting the Swirlyflo tests, were carrying out indicator trials with Caprotti fitted class '5s' of the LMS pattern. Vic Roberts, who was in charge of the indicating operations, having left Ernest Sharp to deal with the Holyhead runs, was most co-operative when I asked if I could have a run to Shrewsbury and back with No. 44687 on the afternoon of 4th November. The engine had, of course, been fitted with an indicating shelter in front of the smokebox, because this was using the Dobie-Mcinnes pattern indicators, so the operators foresook the comfort that I had known with the Farnborough device.

It was a fine afternoon, but I still wrapped up well in overalls and a donkey jacket. I clambered up through the narrow doorway, into the confined space, which was quite warm due to the smokebox. The engine had No. 1 Dynamometer Car in tow, and we set off from Crewe, turning right over the freight lines and past Gresty Lane GW shed, heading for Shrewsbury. Indicator cards on a Mcinnes indicator can be produced in a few seconds, being taken on a piece of paper fitted on to the drum, the diagram being produced by a stylus pressed on to the paper, which had a sensitised surface, where pressure produced a mark. The stylus moved vertically in response to steam pressure, while the drum oscillated in synchronism with the crosshead and hence the piston. A lever driven by the crosshead produced the necessary reduction to the cord drive on to the drum. This drive could be disconnected so that the cards could be fitted and removed from the drum.

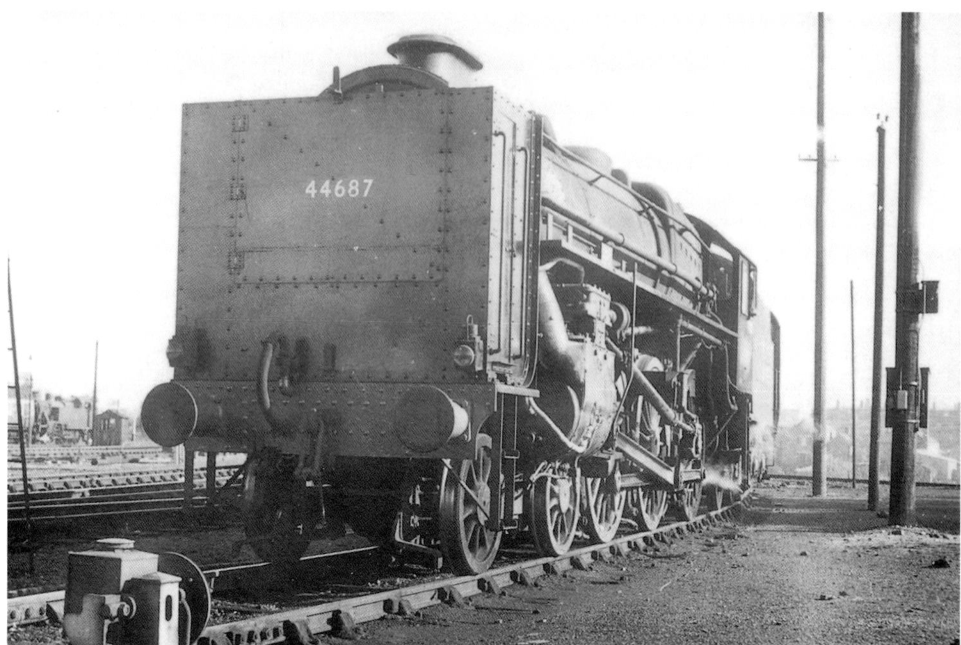

Above: Ex-LMS class '5' 4-6-0 No. 44687 at Shrewsbury near English Bridge Junction on 30th October, 1953. The steam chest pressure pipe is clearly visible.
P. Baker

Right: A close up of class '5' No. 44687 on 30th October, 1953, showing the pendulum lever to the Dobie-Mcinnes indicator drum and steam pipes from the rear cylinder cover and steam chest. The door into the indicator shelter is clearly visible.
P. Baker

Diagrams were taken by signalling from the shelter to the cab that the operator was ready, and the inspector would instruct the driver as to the required cut-off, which was then set, and the regulator opened wide. The card was taken and OK signalled to the cab, the regulator closed, and the next card in sequence checked. A pre-arranged series was agreed before departure, with certain hand signals being used if a repeat was needed. At long cut-offs and full regulator, acceleration was fairly sharp, but as the card only took a short time, the speed fell away again during coasting before the next record was made.

I found it fascinating to see how it was all done, using a changeover valve to produce front and back cylinder diagrams, and the steam chest pressure line. The speed was provided from the dynamometer car, although I think this particular engine was speedometer fitted too. One of the most remarkable things I found was that one could put one's head above the top of the shelter - it was open at the top and the air was quite still. But put your hand forward over the front sheet, and you knew the direction of air flow with a vengeance. On reaching Shrewsbury, we turned on the triangle via Abbey Foregate and English Bridge Junctions. After a short time we set off back to Crewe, taking several more cards during the return journey.

My experience on the footplate of Southern locomotives over metals was nil at this time, but I managed to break my duck at the end of 1953 when, accompanied by Pat Webb, we set off to explore the Kent & East Sussex Railway (K&ESR). I did not have the advantage of a footplate pass on this occasion, but I was able to persuade the driver of No. 34075 *264 Squadron* at Charing Cross to take me aboard for a run to Headcorn. I was threatened with the shovel, of course but when I said I would like to have a go, the door was opened. The cab impressed me immediately by its

Bulleid Light Pacific, 'West Country' class No. 34091 *Weymouth* at Stewarts Lane on 27th April, 1950. I had a footplate trip on another Light Pacific, No. 34075 *264 Squadron*, from Charing Cross to Headcorn on 12th December, 1953. *Author*

'N2' class No. 69581 at the platform alongside Alexandra Palace in North London. *Author*

The fireman's side view from ex-LNER 'A4' class Pacific No. 60013 *Dominion of New Zealand* somewhere between Hatfield and Grantham on 12th June, 1954. Unfortunately I did not record the precise location! *Author*

spaciousness, and the fireman, hearing that I was from Derby, proudly showed me the electric lights, and the steam operated 'butterfly' firedoors. In action, *264 Squadron* was quite impressive too, with its soft exhaust, despite quite a big train which had the engine right at the platform end. I had a turn with the shovel and found the firedoor quite easy except when I was trying to put a bit in the back corners. My foot slipped off the pedal on the floor, and the doors grabbed hold of the shaft of the shovel. I soon had them open again, and the fireman said, 'It's OK mate, there's not many who don't do that when they first come on one of these'.

All too soon we were at Headcorn, and I stepped down, watching No. 34075 start away before turning to investigate the charms of the K&ESR which in those days still provided a link between the Folkestone and Hastings lines.

The middle of the following year saw me back at Hatfield to carry on the 'N2' saga. In the interim period, one engine, No. 69579, had been fitted with modified springing, the leading and trailing springs having 18 plates instead of the standard 12, and the same 18 plate springs replacing the standard coil springs on the driving axle. For comparison, No. 69580 was also fresh out of shops, and allocated to Hatfield for the tests. The modified engine was an improvement, and had less tendency to roll and felt more comfortable. This spell was relatively short as it was felt that both engines would be good riding, and the intention was to make an assessment when a considerable mileage had been accumulated, with both engines. Bill Cattermole was going to try to keep the mileages similar to help with the evaluation.

One day, having done two round trips to Dunstable, I then set off to Kings Cross on another 'N2', came back to Finsbury Park and fitted in a trip up to Alexandra Palace and back on yet another 'N2' before returning to Hatfield, quite late in the evening. As it was mid-June, it made a pleasant, albeit long day, and enabled me to ink in another line on the map taken out of a *Bradshaw*.

At the end of the week, I decided to come home via Grantham, as there was a train stopping at Hatfield, and then Hitchin, Huntingdon, Peterborough and Grantham before going on to York. I had not thought of riding on the footplate this day, until the train came into view as it rounded the curve south of Hatfield. It was an 'A4', No. 60013 *Dominion of New Zealand* and once again my footplate pass came in handy. I was made welcome as usual, and thoroughly enjoyed the trip, which was a bonus that I had not expected.

In October, I found myself back on the Carlisle-Skipton route once more, this time to test out a boiler water level indicator which was based on use of radioactive cobalt. It was always a problem with the mobile test plant to correct the reading on the water gauge at beginning and end of a test, to allow for gradient and other variables. Some quite tedious calculations were necessary - I know because I have done some - to work out how much water the boiler held in each one inch 'layer' through the water space over the six or seven inches of the gauge glass. Readers will understand that the curvature of the boiler shell meant that there was a reducing quantity in the layers as you went from bottom to top of the glass. The calculations had to take into account rivet heads, stays and other features in the boiler. Every boiler I had to calculate was a taper boiler too, and we had no electronic calculators in those days. Vic Roberts decreed that a slide rule was not accurate enough, so it was a case of logarithm tables. As I said, very tedious.

BR Standard class '9' 2-10-0 No. 92013 standing on the Ilkley line at Skipton prior to returning to Carlisle on 7th October, 1954. The author was involved in testing a water level indicator based on radioactive cadmium. No. 3 Dynamometer Car is the first vehicle in the train. *Author*

The device I was involved with was intended to cut out the need for correction of the level, as it was located at the centre of gravity of the boiler water mass covered by the water gauge. It consisted of a length of radioactive cobalt wire about 10 in. long, held in a length of tube, which was screwed into a wash-out plug which was in turn fitted into the boiler shell close to the vertical centre line through the boiler and longitudinally at the centre of gravity. The engine on test was one of the Standard 2-10-0s, No. 92013 and I had a week with my ex-colleagues in the locomotive testing section. I provided them with data from the scintillation counter which was clamped to the handrail to pick up the radiation from the source, being wired back into the dynamometer car. At the end of the week, there was an excellent correlation between my readings and their readings off the water gauge, after correction. However, as was often the case, no further use was made of the radioactive device; we in the Research Department formed the opinion that if George Stephenson had not used the system, then the CME Department would not use it either!

February 1955 brought me into direct contact with the steam locomotive again. At the time, we were involved in braking system trials, and the practical aspects were covered by runs on two Sundays a fortnight apart in February from Toton to Bedford and back. The power was two class '9s', with 70 loaded 16 ton mineral wagons giving a trailing load of 1,700 tons plus. I rode on the train engine, with Pat Webb on the pilot. There was a locomotive inspector on each engine, George Brownlow and Reg Haynes being the two individuals concerned. It was quite incredible to notice the difference in style of the two men. George tended to be a bit 'dapper' - he always wore a pair of cotton gloves, and a white shirt, and he must have repelled coal dust in some way, as he would climb down at the end of the day looking quite fresh and remarkably clean considering where he had been.

Reg - or Mechanical Mac as he was known - was just the opposite. Five minutes on a moving locomotive and he was as black as the Ace of Spades. Well, maybe not five minutes, but not much longer! Reg was at his best in the cab, and he was rarely standing watching; he was either driving or firing. It was just coming daylight as we pulled out of Toton Yard, on a freezing morning, amid clouds of steam. The train took a bit of starting, but in due time, we were away and had an uneventful run, with smooth braking during the tests. The train was vacuum fitted, each wagon having two brake cylinders, only one of which was used when they were in tare condition, a manual lever being used to select the loaded or empty setting. I had been involved with some of the initial tests with these wagons, and we had come a long way from the bumps and bangs we had in those days.

On reaching Bedford, we detached the engines from the train, and crossed the main line onto the shed. The arrangement was that two sets of Bedford men would service the engines, cleaning fires, coaling the tender and filling the tank, finally turning them and coupling them together while the Toton men had their meal and a brew. However, it turned out that a hiccup had occurred, and there were no men available. 'Right', says Reg, 'We'll do them ourselves'. Ourselves was Reg, Pat and me. Reg would not hear of the Toton men doing it, and it was not George's scene. So it was that Pat and I took one class '9', Reg took the other and we set to over the ash pit, under the coaling plant, up to the water column and finally on to the turntable. Between us, and with a bit of to-ing and fro-ing to give Reg a hand like getting the bag in, we were ready in good time. Cans of tea appeared with the engine crews, and sandwiches were demolished, complete with black fingermarks as we moved off to collect our train. A most enjoyable interlude. And a fortnight later we had a repeat performance! Men had been booked on that occasion, but some emergency had arisen and they had all had to go off somewhere so we did it all again. The foreman used the Nelson's eye as to who was driving engines round the yard, of course.

The journey home on this occasion was not without incident either. We had set off from Bedford up the slow lines past Sharnbrook and Souldrop and as we were going through the tunnel, there was a snatch which nearly threw me off balance, and a loud bang. As we emerged into daylight, we stopped to examine and make sure all was well. In fact it was not. The front coupling on the train engine had been damaged and the hook was pulled right forward so that instead of pointing towards the smokebox, it pointed to the sky. The pilot engine had felt the lurch too, but we could find no cause for it. The wagons were all in order as far as we could see, so we put the train engine shackle on to the pilot coupling and proceed cautiously to Wellingborough where a thorough examination was carried out. We reversed the engines to put the damaged hook at the front and, having been assured that nothing untoward had been found, we went on our merry way, about two hours behind schedule. Our route was via Manton and Melton Mowbray on these runs, of course, rather than the direct line from Glendon Junction to Leicester and Syston.

All this extra activity at lunchtime resulted in not only Reg, but also Pat and myself being as black as if we had just come out of a coal mine. It washed off, anyway, although both Pat and I had black rimmed eyes for a day or two. I personally thought it was worth it, for the chance to drive a class '9', even if it was only semi-legal and only in a shed yard, I was still in charge of a full size steam locomotive.

BR Standard 'Britannia' class 4-6-2s Nos. 70043 and 70044 in the up slow platform at Kettering with a train of 70 16 ton 'Minfit' wagons loaded with coal, on a Toton to Brent test run in 1955.
P. Webb

BR Standard class '5' 4-6-0s Nos. 73030 and 73031 with a train made up of the carriage & wagon department test car, fifty 16 ton 'Minfit' wagons and a brake van, ready for a run from Toton Sidings to Brent, Cricklewood in 1955.
P. Webb

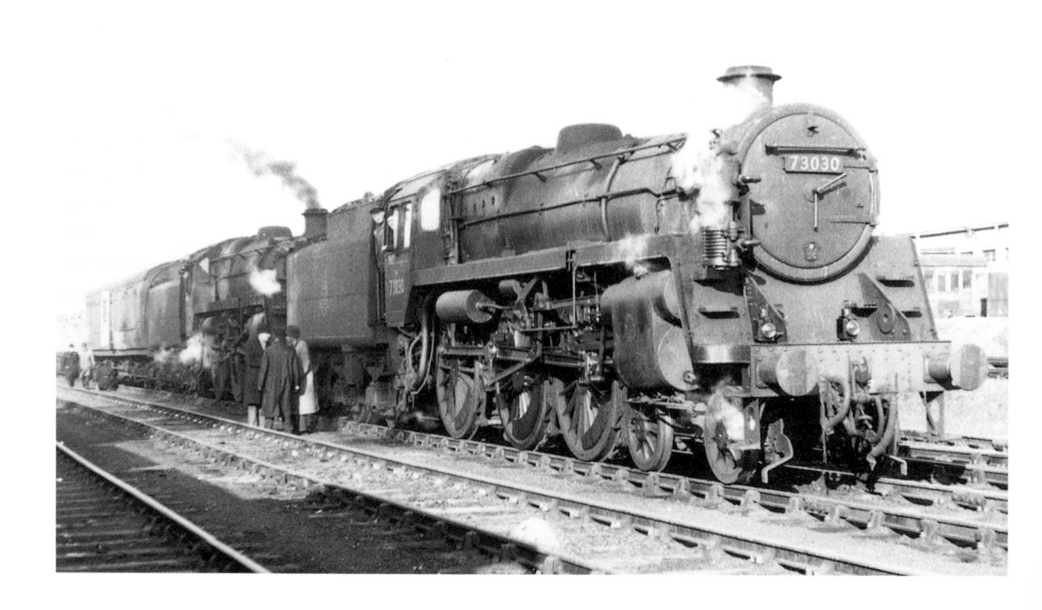

Chapter Eleven

Steam Finale

At the end of the last chapter I was recounting experiences with brake trial trains. These in fact were towards the end of a series of tests, spread over several years, involving both vacuum- and Westinghouse-fitted 16 ton mineral wagons. All these trains were steam-hauled, and the air-braked trains were handled by a pair of Standard class '5' engines, fitted with Westinghouse pumps and brake equipment, or by two 'Britannias', Nos. 70043/4, whose appearance was transformed by removal of the smoke deflectors, and the mounting of an air pump at each side of the smokebox towards the front.

We had some problems with both types of brake at times. I recall one trip with 70 vacuum braked wagons, hauled by two LMS class '5' locomotives when the brake was 'unstable'. The destruction of the vacuum to apply the brake was not effected by admitting all the air required through the driver's brake valve; this admission altered the vacuum level in the train pipe and this change then triggered what was known as a direct admission valve, which admitted air directly to the brake cylinder. The propagation rate along the train pipe was quite rapid so that the brakes at the rear of the train were applied only a few seconds after those at the front. We had carried out a lot of tests with a static train, using different choke plates in the system, to get the best application conditions. However, on the day in question, with the train on the move, it did not function as it was supposed to, and we had one or two problems. We were testing on the Toton to Brent run and had passed Kettering without incident when we came up to the Burton Latimer distant which was on. I was on the leading engine, and the driver applied his brake gently, as he would to make an initial application to check speed slightly. The vacuum gauge fell to 14 inches and then suddenly dropped to zero. By this time the signal had cleared, but the train came to a pretty rapid stop. What had happened was that one of the direct admission valves had opened, and that was sufficient to admit more air to the system, and that was that. The trouble was that with two brake cylinders per wagon, it took ages to exhaust the system ready for a re-start. Eventually, even by using the large ejectors on both locomotives - strictly against the book - we got away. Fortunately we had no more adverse signals, and the inspector and driver realised that on arrival, careful judgment would be necessary to bring the train to a stand, by virtually only one application of the brake. The judgment was perfect and we stopped only a few yards short of our signal. 'Better short than past it' was the inspector's comment.

The return journey was fine as far as Leicester, as we realised that, provided we did not reduce below 15 inches, we had a perfectly controllable brake. However, approaching Leicester, the driver took a fraction too much and away it went, bringing us to a stand with the engines right alongside London Road signal box. As we had clear signals and were just checking for the speed restriction through the station, the signalman at first thought something was wrong. When we said that all was OK, he grew visibly more irate as we stood 'blowing up'. He was just about apoplectic when we moved off after 14 minutes! Needless to say, further work to overcome the problem started the next day, which I think involved vacuum reservoirs on each wagon. We had no repetitions, anyway.

The Westinghouse train was not immune from gremlins either, although generally it was a much better brake giving smooth stops and a rapid release, even on these big trains. But it did find a weakness in the carriage and wagon engineer's test car one day. We were heading for home north of Leicester at a fair clip when, just as we approached Barrow-on-Soar, there was a lurch and the brakes went on hard. I was in the test car at the time, and when we were stationary, someone slid back the vestibule door. What a sight met our eyes! The train had divided and about 200 yards ahead of us were the two Standard class '5' engines, while not five yards in front, lay the headstock of the coach with the splintered remains of the end panel. Fortunately, it must have bounced along, attached to the tender coupling for some distance before it broke away. Good job it did too, because if we had run into it, we could have had hundreds of tons of coal slack down our necks! Fifty loaded 16 ton wagons of coal makes a big pile!

The beginning of August 1955 saw me yet again varying my route to London, this time by going to Wellingborough, hence to Northampton, and on to Euston. My destination was once more Hatfield for the final comparison between Nos. 69579 and 69580. It was arranged that I had '79 one day and '80 the next with Hatfield to Luton and Hatfield to Dunstable trips on each day. Now that they had run a good mileage, the modified engine No. 69579 having covered approximately 59,000 miles, while the standard No. 69580 had clocked up 56,000 miles, the comparison was easier to make. The modified locomotive could still display the odd violent movement but without pitching or rolling, while points and crossing did not cause undue discomfort to be felt on the footplate. The sister engine was much worse riding, and tended to nose and roll considerably. Conditions on the footplate, I recorded as 'quite uncomfortable, and occasionally alarming, on one occasion causing the driver to close the regulator and apply the brake'.

So it seemed that the modification was a success, although the cost of conversion was given as the reason for not proceeding with a programme to modify further engines. What did I say about George Stephenson last time?

My return to Derby was from Paddington to Birmingham Snow Hill, via Bicester on the footplate of 'Castle' class 4-6-0 No. 5032 *Usk Castle*. I had, of course, hoped for a 'King', but it was not to be. My first impressions were 'what stops me from falling off?' I was used to the substantial doors of LMS engines, and here all there seemed to be was a couple of handrails and a bit of chain! Once I got used to it, I paid more attention to the rest of the cab layout. Quite different from what I was used to with only one gauge glass, displacement lubrication, coils of tube in the cab roof; and the firedoor was only just above the cab floor or so it seemed. Also, the tender was much lower than what I regarded as normal. It was a beautifully smooth, quiet engine, although of course, it didn't half bark on starting. I had a go with the shovel, but found it awkward to fire 'downhill' when I was used to a firehole around knee high. However, I watched the fireman for a spell and then asked if I could try again, and I think I coped a lot better the second time.

At one stage on the journey, the driver turned and said 'hold on tight'. A few seconds later, the engine pitched violently to the left and then came upright again. He turned to me again: '20 mph there up to two days ago. Now it's been taken off. Bit rough, isn't it?' I agreed it was; we were doing about 75 mph at the time, and if I had been the driver, I reckon I would have slackened off a bit.

All too soon we were passing Tyseley and emerging from the tunnel into Snow Hill station, which had always been a favourite of mine. I bade the crew farewell - they were going on to Wolverhampton - and made my way across town to the black smoky hole called New Street, and so back to Derby.

A lot of my work was now being directed towards the riding of vehicles and in November I spent a fortnight riding in the brake van at the back of fish trains from Aberdeen to Edinburgh. Tom Rhead had evolved a theory that hot axleboxes on wagons were associated with tight end clearance between the journal and the bearing. What I had to do was observe vans along the train, using a telescope if necessary, and then at Dundee and Edinburgh, check axlebox temperatures by touching a hand to them. Tom's idea was that the vehicles which moved about a lot, and so had bigger clearances, would be cooler. I went round the train each morning with the carriage and wagon examiner to get a rough idea of the degree of wear in the axleboxes, and over the fortnight it seemed that Tom's ideas were on the right lines. We had one or two wagons to detach at Dundee and Edinburgh because they were hot, and generally these had been noted as steady riders.

I should apologise, I suppose, as this has nothing to do with steam engines. Or at least very little. Maybe I was at the wrong end of the train, but the effort put out at the front, generally by a 'V2' could be observed very clearly. And did those trains run? There were two, sometimes three every day, big trains they were too. I needed about four hands and arms at times. One to hang on, one to

Ex-Great North of Scotland Railway 'Z4' class 0-4-2T on the fish quays at Aberdeen in November 1955. At the time I was involved with fish van riding observations. Probably the smelliest job I ever did! *Author*

hold the telescope, one to write and another to hang on! A brake van at 70-plus can be lively indeed. The train went on from Edinburgh to London, but I returned to Aberdeen. And some funny looks I got too, as the scent (?) of fish seemed to cling to me. Certainly when I got home at weekends, I was made to hang those clothes which were not to be washed outside to air!

My next involvement with the steam locomotive was once again as a footplate observer. We were developing methods of measuring accelerations on vehicles to give a quantitative aspect to ride measurements and we wanted to run some tests at 90 mph. A three-coach train was used, hauled by Compound No. 40927, running between Derby and Knighton, Saffron Lane near Leicester where there was a triangle which assisted with turning. The line through Chaddesden Sidings at Derby was then still open, so it was possible to run straight through Derby Midland from either end and continue back to Leicester. Two round trips were made each day for a week, and we managed the 90 every time in the down direction through Loughborough. A Compound was a fairly rough engine at that sort of speed and tended to crash and bang violently over points and crossings, and there were some of those at Loughborough. One's retention in the cab was ensured by a very similar arrangement to that on *Usk Castle*, just a length of chain, and the similarity continued with a low tender compared to a Stanier engine.

On the locomotive itself, the footplate was quite narrow, owing to the intrusion of the rear wheel splasher. The driver's seat was in fact on top of the reverser, not that the seat was used at all, as the vibration made it too uncomfortable. It was interesting to see the operation of the regulator, by which the driver selected whether he was running as a simple or a compound engine. My duties precluded any chance to have a go at firing, but it did not appear difficult, with a good thick fire which was rarely fuelled when we were running at speed. I think the whole week could best be summed up as 'exhilarating'.

About a month later we ran a similar test using accelerometers, but this time to check the response to poor quality track and on a freight vehicle too. The train was a 'Big Goods' '4F' 0-6-0 No. 44017, hauling a lowmac wagon and a brake van. Once again I was on the footplate over a route which was mainly freight only, going from Derby to Ambergate, Pye Bridge Junction, Kirkby, Mansfield South and East Junctions, Southwell, Farnsfield Junction to Rolleston Junction. As far as I recall, it was possible to turn on the triangle whose other leg was at Fiskerton Junction, and this manoeuvre we made, before retracing the same route home. There was even less room on the 'Big Goods' than on the Compound, but we were not running at any speed except between Derby and Ambergate, where we got up towards a mile a minute. Not for long, fortunately, and with a light load, so those so-vulnerable leading axleboxes did not give any trouble.

Steam work now became very thin on the ground, with a lot of my time being spent on checking tyre wear on coaches, which were put on circuits where we could keep an eye on them. I was also involved with similar work on the Southern Region on multiple units. When opportunity presented itself, I would use a different route, as when I had to go to Cardiff, and went via New Street and Snow Hill, then Stourbridge, Kidderminster, Hereford and Pontypool Road. Unfortunately I did not have a footplate pass on these expeditions, and had to content myself with the change of scenery.

It was two years after the '4F' trip before we had any further steam involvement. This was in May 1958, between York and Darlington when we did two round trips with coaches fitted with Commonwealth bogies. The train was hauled by 'A1'class Pacific No. 60128 *Bongrace* and the main object of the exercise was to reach 100 mph on each of the four runs. That target was achieved comfortably, and I was able to have a footplate ride on the third run to Darlington. It was a great experience, and the enthusiasm of the footplate crew who could only run at these speeds by breaking the rules was terrific. The engine had been selected for the job in hand and was naturally in tip-top condition. It made light of the five-coach train, and rode very well, much better than the sister engine on which I went from Grantham to Kings Cross some years before. The train was turned via the Geneva triangle at Darlington, and used the avoiding line from Skelton Bridge Junction and York Yard North to come back behind York station for the second down run. Our average speeds for each run were all above 70 mph, quite an achievement in those days, although electric train schedules of today make them appear almost slow! But where is the skill in coaxing power out of an electric locomotive? They either go, or don't, with no requirement for effort from the driver to get a better result.

I was wrong at the beginning of the last paragraph to say there was a two year desert for steam. Poring over my log, I realise that I missed a series of tests on the Southern Region near Basingstoke. A new high speed turn-out had been installed, and we were asked to assist in its evaluation, using accelerometers to measure lateral forces on the coaching stock. The actual site was at Worting Junction, and we made runs in the down direction at speeds of up to 70 mph, starting from either Basingstoke or Hook, and terminating the runs at Micheldever where the locomotive ran round. We had a 'Merchant Navy' for these trials, but I do not seem to have made a note of the engine number. Four runs occupied two days and everyone was satisfied with the performance of the train over the junction. I did not get a chance for a footplate run even on the up runs when we were going back for our next try. But I did hear a 'Merchant Navy' being driven hard to reach the speeds required.

There then was two years again after No. 60128 until steam appeared again, when I was involved on some freight train tests between Somers Town and Rotherham. It just happened that these trains were still steam-hauled; as with the Aberdeen Fish, our instruments were installed in the brake van at the rear. And what a ride we had. From Leagrave to Bedford on the long downhill run, I timed the train at over 70! We only had the one run so I did not find out if it was typical, although the guard said that some drivers tended to 'leather it' on that stretch. The rest of the run was quite stirring too and the Stanier '5' on the front was certainly being worked hard. It came dark about Leicester, and we could see the fireworks as we thrashed up the Erewash Valley.

April/May 1961 produced what turned out to be my penultimate involvement with steam locomotives on a test train. At this time, the four-wheel pallet vans were gaining themselves a notorious reputation for bad riding and derailment, and an effort was being made to see if steps could be taken to solve the problem. This produced four footplate trips for me between Annesley and Woodford, over the Great Central line on Standard class '5' engines. I was able to do a bit of firing too, and it proved to be a very enjoyable series of runs. One impression that sticks in my mind even today was the cathedral-like spaciousness of Nottingham Victoria as the train emerged from the tunnels at each end. While I had been there many times before, it had always been in the train, and the different view-point on the footplate produced this effect, in which the locomotive seemed dwarfed under the great roof.

Another memory of those trips was the 'ringing' of the engine wheels. When coasting, it was particularly evident, and the effect seemed to be associated with the rail joints providing sufficient of a blow to make the wheel ring quite clearly. I had never noticed it before, and the inspector who was with me said he had heard it, but never on any other class of engine. I could not recall it with No. 73008 over the Settle-Carlisle line, but it happened regularly every day on these tests, even though three different locomotives were used over the four days. The last time I can claim steam haulage of a test train was when we were making measurements of palletised traffic between Carlisle and Hellifield. The train was a special with a recording vehicle at the front, with wires to instruments in three or four vans behind it, so that steps had to be taken to turn the train for the return journey. By this time, diesels were making themselves very much felt, and we had a Mirrlees Type 2 for the run from Carlisle. I fully expected this engine to take us from Hellifield to Blackburn, where the train was to reverse, then run to Skipton, reverse again, and then Hellifield and back to Carlisle.

So it was with some surprise, and considerable pleasure, that on arrival at Hellifield I was informed that the men were not trained on diesels and a 'Black 5' was going to take over. This was a bonus indeed. As No. 45318 coupled to the train, I introduced myself to the driver, and asked if I could accompany him. He made some disparaging remarks about the condition of the engine, but assured me I was welcome. He was right, of course, and No. 45318 was far from comfortable, with a tremendous knock in the trailing axleboxes and clouds of steam which came from below the cab floor. The Stanier hooter was badly out of tune too, and probably would not have been heard above the noise of the locomotive when on the move! But it was steam, hot, oily, dusty as many a steam locomotive could be. Blackburn came all too soon, and we ran round the train, and it was then that I made a mistake. I decided to stay put and ride to Skipton. As soon as we got up to about 25 miles an hour, coal dust started to literally billow out of the tender into the cab, and in a very short time, everything was black with it. The fireman fetched a few shovelfuls down to fill the hole at the shovelling plate but by then the damage was done. He said it was more dust than coal and I had noticed that it was very small when he was firing to Blackburn.

On arrival at Skipton we had to run round again, but as I was leaving the train at Hellifield in the charge of one of my colleagues, I decided that I had better try and remove some of the grime in the coach. One of the other chaps took my place, of course, as chances like this were rare indeed.

And that was that. Steam never figured again in the course of my testing work, and I am pretty certain that No. 45318 worked the last steam-hauled test train on BR (even if we were not testing at the time!). I can only hope that readers have found my story of some interest, and that I have been able to convey some of the great times that I have enjoyed with Steam.